EVERYTHING
I WISH I'D
KNOWN

ABOUT

STRESS

Also by Jayne Hardy

The Self-Care Project
365 Days of Self-Care
Making Space
Kind Words for Unkind Days

EVERYTHING I WISH I'D KNOWN

ABOUT
STRESS

A Hopeful Toolkit

JAYNE HARDY

floe.

First published in Great Britain in 2023 by Floe Publishing
Old Stables, Harewood,
Calstock PL18 9SQ

Front cover design by Beth Free at Studio Nicandlou

A CIP catalogue record for this book is
Available from the British Library.
ISBN (Hardback) 978 1 7392586 0 3
ISBN (eBook) 978 1 7392586 1 0
Printed and bound in Great Britain by Clays Ltd, Elcograf S.p.A

Page 116-122 core values list reproduced by permission of
The Berkeley Wellbeing Institute

floe.

www.floepublishing.co.uk

*Dedicated to my husband, Dom,
and our daughter, Peggy*

Contents

My own road to a calmer life 1

Part One, or 'I wish I'd known. . .'.. 9

Some stress is normal – we're literally built for it 11
Chronic stress has been normalised 13
But it is not normal 15
There's such a thing as good stress 17
Fight and flight aren't the only stress responses 19
Stress can even change our menstrual cycles 21
We store stress in the body 23
How the nervous system works 25
How to hack the nervous system 27
Stress causes damage that can be deadly 29
All the symptoms of stress 31
The red flags 33
Stress and anxiety are not the same thing 35
Stress is contagious 37
Our perspective makes a difference 39
We all have different stress thresholds 41
What stress can look like in others 43
Stress erodes our capacity for empathy 46
Stress affects our executive functioning 48
Stress can become a habit 50
What we consume can aggravate stress 52

Stress and resilience are intertwined 54
The concept of the stress bucket 56
Spoon theory 58
The notion of stress cycles 61

Part Two 63

In the thick of it 64
  And breathe. 65
    Square breathing 65
    Ten-second breath 66
    Alternate nostril 66
    Four-seven-eight breathing 67
    Cyclic sighing 68
  Get grounded 69
    Five, four, three, two, one technique 69
    Positive self-talk 70
    Counting 71
    A–Z game 71
    Embracing nature 71
  Use our common sense(s) 74
    Touch 74
    Smell 75
    Taste 76
    Sight 77
    Sound 78
    Proprioception 79
    Interoception 79
    Vestibular 81
    Somatic practices 82
    Tapping 83
    Autonomous sensory meridian response (ASMR) 85
  The aftermath 87
    Shake it off 88
    Stretch it out 89

Dance it out 90
Talk it out 91
Cry it out 92
Write it out 93
Building resilience 100
Make space for yourself 101
Track time 102
Buy time 104
Start subtracting 106
Look ahead 107
Keep a stress log 108
Visualise your stress bucket 110
Build your self-esteem 112
Get clear on your values 115
Smartphones for good 123
Turn off notifications 123
Blue light filter 124
Apps 124
Start a new hobby 127
Get moving 129
Stop the ANTs 130
Consider adaptogens 133
Try meditating 135
Fix your sleep 137
Pack your bag 139
Check-in 140
Write a care guide 143
A note on support systems 146
Healing 148
Seven types of rest 149
Mental rest 150
Physical rest 150
Sensory rest 150
Creative rest 151
Emotional rest 151

Spiritual rest 152
Create a bliss list 153
Create a diss list 154
Question whether we're headed in the right direction 155
Make sense of something 160
Let go of mistakes 162
Get clear on who you are not 163
Lock it in 165
Reset your algorithm 167
Be the tryer of new things 169
Pay attention to envy 171
Reclaiming yourself 172
Dream a little dream 174
Consider the younger self 176
Be your own compass 178
Have those conversations 180
I wish I'd known that I wasn't alone 181
It's always a work in progress 184
Food as medicine 184
Movement 185
Other daily stuff 185
Working life 187
Can't live without 187
Over to you 189

Acknowledgements 191
About the author 193

Introduction

Do you lay your head down on your pillow at night as restless thoughts whizz around between your ears? Do you find it impossible to unwind, to relax, to chill out, to focus on one thing at a time? Does your brain feel full: of noise, of endless to-do lists, of ruminating, of ideas, of everything, anything, and nothing? Are you living with mysterious aches and pains and a whole host of other 'odd' physical sensations and ailments? Do you perpetually feel exhausted or as though life is spinning out of control?

I'm hazarding a not-so-wild guess that you might be answering with a lot of yeses – you've got this book in your hands, after all.

In a world that's always 'on', it's becoming increasingly difficult to switch off, to distinguish between our differing roles, to hold a firm sense of identity, to feel well. We've got used to the insomnia, the chasing of tails, and of never really feeling as though we're 'done', even as we hang up our boots, laptops, and/or bags for the day. All of this comes with a relentless inner (and sometimes outer) dialogue that we're only valuable for the value we bring, that we're not enough, and that we should do and be more.

I want to remind you that *you* aren't lacking in any way and that you're not audacious for wanting more for yourself. Living a life that's got stress stampeding rampantly through it is miserable. And nobody (including you) deserves that.

Stress has become so normalised nowadays that I don't think we realise *just* how stressed we are. It's as if slowly, over time, the stress-bar has been raised, and it's commonplace to be frazzled. We've got used to it and so have those around us. At the same time, we *can* feel it all around us, that sense of unease, urgency, and, as though things are off-kilter.

So we're going to intentionally untangle ourselves from the busyness; we're going to consider, reflect, and be thoughtful in how we dismantle whatever it is that has led us to the point of distress. We'll learn about the whys and whatnots that brought us here, we'll meet ourselves where we are, and we'll delve into coping strategies and tools to ensure we move ahead in a way that works for us personally.

The first part of the book is written to help you understand the whys and whatnots about stress, the mechanics, the science, the mental and physical aspects – all the things I wish I'd known. It's with this knowledge, I hope, that you will be able to gain a new perspective on stress, to address and redress it, and then to feel more equipped and motivated to make changes.

As the first part of the book underpins the *why*, the second part contains things to *try*, so that you too can build a collection of tools to help you through to a calmer and clearer state of mind. In the moments we feel the most helpless, I think it's helpful to have actionable things we can do, action being the antithesis of that horrid sense of helplessness and hopelessness.

It is written to meet you where you are. You'll be guided through ways you can ease the stress whilst you're in the very thick of it and ways you can address it, longer term. When we're at that totally frazzled stage, all we need is a reprieve, a breather, a break, and I'm hoping that Part Two brings ways for you to find that. You'll find just enough self-helpfulness to get you to a place where the learning and understanding *can* sink in.

So, here it is, a hopeful toolkit from me to you.

My own road to a calmer life

Because I'm the sort to bottle up my feelings, it's difficult to isolate exactly when stress became an issue for me. I suspect it was at that ripe old age of 18 when we're left to make our own decisions about what comes next. There was always a sense that I was ill-equipped for that. No career option seemed to 'fit' or interest me but the pressure to choose something, anything, felt stifling, as though it was urgent that I get it all figured out. Little did I know that I still wouldn't really have it all 'figured out' some 20-odd years later!

I distinctly remember our careers adviser encouraging us to join the military or go to university and neither of those options inspired me. Never in my wildest dreams did I imagine I could be an author or lead workshops or mentor and support people. Those things wouldn't have ever felt possible or realistic for me and so accountancy it was.

Oh, boy.

There's so much about that time in my life that just didn't 'fit'. My personal life was rife with dysfunctional relationships and unhealthy habits. Professionally, I wasn't suited to working in an open-plan office, the repetitive nature of the work, but worst of all were the bloody timesheets! We'd have to account for our time to make sure clients were billed correctly – in six-minute increments. If we logged too much administrative time, it was noticed and mentioned (I never did work out what to do with loo breaks!). You couldn't obviously charge non-client time to a client, although I'm sure that did happen at times. It was bewildering to me, this environment where productivity, efficiency and charge rates were of utmost importance.

This is nothing new. We all have similar stories to tell of these environments where what we do matters more than who we are. Those years though, as well as feeling constrictive, felt formative. So, *this* is what working life is all about. I thought it was the norm. I sadly think it *still* is the norm, all too often.

One Monday morning, I fell down the stairs on my way to work and busted my elbow, dislocating and fracturing the radial head. The week before, I'd handed in my notice and ended up spending my notice period in hospital, recovering from an operation which saw my radial head replaced with a titanium fixture.

For want of some life-direction. I decided I'd head to university to study business management.

What a mistake-er to make-er.

Again, it didn't 'fit'. The drinking culture was such a lot, and I've never actually handled alcohol well. My course was so utterly boring. It felt purposeless too, so I didn't have any sense of direction. It was a 'just-because' decision that I made in haste and without giving myself time and space to explore who I was and what I'd truly like to do next.

I travelled home for the Easter holidays and told Dad I didn't want to go back to university. 'Come on then,' he said, 'Let's go and get your stuff.' We zipped up the motorway, grabbed my belongings, and that was it. I was a university dropout, and carried the weight of shame for too long. I did not recognise, back then, the wisdom in quitting something that isn't right for you.

Back to accountancy I went. It was what I knew...

Then, depression hit, and I got signed off work and ultimately lost that job. Mild depression turned to moderate and then to severe depression and it was all I could do just to stay alive.

Somewhere in the darkness, there were lighter times where I'd get another accountancy job, hate it, and then leave. The turning point was working for an electrician, overseeing his accounts. It was whilst working for him that I got to understanding what running a business looked and felt like. It helped that his husky dog would sit with me in the office and that I was mostly left to my own devices. I was also just so chuffed I was holding down a job – it'd been a while!

On the side, my husband Dom and I had started handmaking wedding jewellery and it was doing well. This was pre-social-media, so we'd attend bridal fayres and host jewellery parties. We even managed to get our work in national magazines. We had a website and started having online sales. It was really fun.

Around that time, my boss's business got bought out (or it merged, I can't remember, exactly). All I'd known was accountancy and so I started a bookkeeping business. Very, very quickly, I had too many clients to handle, and Dom left his job to work with me. There was a point where we had to choose whether we wanted to focus on the jewellery or the bookkeeping. We chose what felt more stable and sensible than what felt like pure joy. Bookkeeping won out.

I think it'd have been more okay if we'd known about boundaries back then. We had zero and the impact on my mental health was tremendously detrimental. Clients would call us at all hours, and we'd answer. I remember being on maternity leave with Peggy, when she was only a couple of days old, and a client rang (knowing I'd just had a baby) and asked that I go to his premises and re-install his payroll software that he'd inadvertently uninstalled. I was sitting on the cold hard chair with my few-days-old baby and a few-days-old stitches in so much pain and exhaustion. It hadn't even occurred to me to say no.

Alongside bookkeeping I had been blogging. Originally a beauty blog where I'd review products. It gradually evolved into being about my experiences of depression. My blog grew quickly and before I knew it, I'd gone and started a charitable organisation. In 2011, The Blurt Foundation was born. Its aims were to raise awareness and understanding of depression. This work totally and utterly changed my life.

We created a self-care subscription box in 2015, called BuddyBox. This financed our work, and I was then 'all in'. It felt like heaven to not be working within the confines of timesheets and client emails at midnight and the rolling deadlines.

The creative output, the autonomy, the purpose, the impact our work was having – gosh, that lifted me through so many of the obstacles! Talking about depression and using my experiences of it was therapeutic. I was using what had felt like such terrible times as a tool for good, which helped hugely. I'll always remain so utterly grateful for the healing of those early years, which showed me the kinds of environments within which I bloomed.

For a few years, work felt truly wonderful, and the stress felt like 'good' stress: motivating, energising and fun.

But too much of anything can be a bad thing. We grew so quickly, I was like a cyclist attempting to drive a Lamborghini, unequipped, bewildered, and frightened. Our community expanded, our team increased, and my head nigh on exploded with all there was to consider. I burnt out, inevitably. I can see now that it *was* inevitable; I was heading towards it for a long time before I arrived there. I'd recover then burn out, recover then burn out, until I knew I couldn't continue because no number of new processes, new hires, tweaks, or flexing seemed to relieve the overflow of stress.

Then came the pandemic. Suddenly, it was all the above plus homeschooling, plus navigating the changing landscape within work, within our team, and our wider community.

The list of the ways in which stress adversely affected my health is a long one, so here are the clipped field notes: mastalgia (more commonly known as breast pain), crushing headaches, loneliness, tension in my shoulders, constant neck and back aches, insomnia, persistent anxiety, weight gain, and the kicker (that finally made me take stock because it scared me so darned much): chest pains.

In 2022, I was standing in our kitchen one January afternoon chatting with my husband and our daughter when, ostensibly out of nowhere, my chest started really hurting with stabbing pains. I honestly thought I was having a heart attack. The look on our daughter's face was one of pure terror and I knew then that something needed to change because she deserved better. I deserved better. We *all* did and do. (The guilt of letting it get to that point is something that's taking a while to fade.) Breaking the stress cycle started to feel incredibly imperative. I was learning about the many ways stress was affecting my health. I was also becoming aware of the longer-term risks if I kept down that road and I wasn't willing to keep on that path.

During a month's sabbatical, I knew that the best thing for me and for the team was for me to leave. Having a month to sit with that decision helped immensely. It gave me the opportunity to talk about it with several trusted people and to get my head around the idea and feel of it.

Leaving my job, the first job I'd loved, didn't feel like an option until I felt all out of options, and it was the only remaining one on the table. I'd unwittingly created a role that outgrew me. One that no longer 'fit'. It was a heart-wrenching time.

Looking back, it's easy to see different courses of action, which could have led to different outcomes; but we don't know how things will turn out until they're... well... turned out. It's too easy to carry regrets but they weigh us down and hold us back (and this literally became my mantra to stop me from ruminating and falling down a rabbit hole).

What came next was that long overdue space and time to explore who I was and what I'd truly like to do next. It was a liminal space, with brainstorming, ideas, notes jotted down, the pulling of threads, and identifying patterns, and tinkering with possibilities. I gave careful consideration to the conditions and circumstances within which I might bloom. After all, it's not that *we're* not enough, not right, for something, it's that it's not enough nor right *for us*.

With hindsight comes that magical trickery where we can see how lots of pieces of the puzzle fit together or where dots have joined, in ways that we can't always see looking ahead. Hindsight is also super useful if we can shift from rumination to reflection. Doing so affords a wealth of knowledge that we can apply to prevent making those same mistakes again.

What I have learned is that living a life that repeatedly compromises us and who we *could* be, is a stressful one. We owe it to ourselves to honour who we are and who we aren't. The stressful times have taught me how to handle stress better, how to increase my stress threshold and build my resilience, how to make life changes, how to identify my needs and get those needs met and has provided me with tools – so many tools – all of which I'm about to share with you. I hope this book will provide you with what you need to help relieve stress and bring more joy and calm into your life.

Part One, or 'I wish I'd known…'

To handle something that feels bigger than us – which stress so often does, especially when it has compounded – it helps to get to know that something, to gain a foundational understanding of what we're dealing with. Moving forward with that knowledge underpins the 'why' of all our new choices, actions, and behaviours which helps us when motivation wanes (a given when we're trying to create new habits).

Sports teams are great at this. They study their opponents to the nth degree until they have a firm grasp on plays, habits, and weaknesses that they can exploit. It's with this knowledge that they feel prepared and informed enough to take on the opposing team and beat them.

My stress became so prevalent that I couldn't see a way through it. It felt ingrained in my daily life and impossible to untwine from. Diving into all the nuances of it yielded insights into what I might do differently, which comprises Part One of this book. I truly believe, though, that it's the acquired comprehension about the ins and outs of stress which have made those behaviours stick in the longer term, thus eking me away from the wired mess I'd become, improving my health and relationships, and increasing the likelihood that I'd undo some of the damage.

Some of the things I learned were shocking, some made me make sense of myself and others, and some were astonishingly insightful.

Which leads nicely into presenting everything I wish I'd known about stress...

Some stress is normal – we're literally built for it

The thing about stress, in and of itself, is that it's a perfectly normal adaptive response, an evolutionary instinctive mechanism that's designed to keep us safe, to keep us alive, to help us survive. When we talk about stress, we're talking about something that's inevitably part and parcel of our lives but with all things considered, we wouldn't want to fully eradicate stress because in the *right* circumstances it's so darned useful, sometimes life-savingly so.

In situations where we feel threatened, compromised, under pressure, uncertain and tasked with something, we'll experience stress; a physical, mental, and emotional response. That stress response, also known as the 'fight or flight' response, floods our body with hormones like cortisol and adrenaline. These hormones give us the extra preparatory oomph that we might need in those coming moments.

Adrenaline's role is to increase heartbeat and breathing rate, expedite how quickly our muscles can use glucose, direct blood to our muscles and extremities, make us sweat, and inhibit the production of insulin. The hormone we might associate the most with stress, cortisol, functions by increasing the amount of glucose in our bloodstreams, aiding the brain to use that glucose more efficiently and effectively, moderating functions that aren't essential in this perceived dangerous situation, as well as diminishing both the growth and reproductive system processes and altering our immune system response and the parts of our brain that commands motivation, mood, and fear.

Stress is advantageous when the response helps us meet the demands on us, when it helps us reach our goals, perform, and escape. The speedy response is what primes us to be faster, sharper, more alert, energised, and stronger, so that we can overcome whatever lies ahead.

Chronic stress has been normalised

We've established that our stress response is a normal function and reaction to threats, danger, and to feeling pressured, overwhelmed, and compromised. What's *not* normal, is for that stress response to be activated over longer periods of time – that is, chronic stress. Sadly, chronic stress has become normalised within society and that's doing us all such a disservice.

Cigna released a report in 2020 that included some staggering statistics:

- Stress-related illness is the biggest health expenditure in the UK, costing the NHS over £11 billion per year.
- Between 60 and 80 per cent of all GP appointments are for stress-related illness.

It's no longer a shock when someone expresses how stressed they are or when burnout is discussed. But it should be. It *should* trigger care, support, and some rallying of the troops.

Yet, when we take into consideration how fast-paced and

demanding society has become, how people are juggling multiple responsibilities in a landscape where social media has become an integral part of life, with the constant comparison-related pressures and 'busyness' badges of honour, it's not much of a surprise. Add on to that the increased competitive nature of life along with the rise of technology and globalisation during a time of economic uncertainty. People are also working longer hours, with burnout becoming a common phenomenon in many (always too many) fields.

We're all just so darned stressed.

And exhausted.

And overwhelmed.

And wrapped up in our own burdensome stuff.

Is it any wonder we're no longer shocked when someone is buckling beneath the weight of it all?

In fact, we feel guilt and shame that we can't cope. We question our ability to cope with an un-cope-able load. rather than questioning the weight of that burden.

Altogether, then, because of the normalisation of stress, when you or I are experiencing heightened and prolonged periods of stress, it doesn't stand out as something that needs addressing with any semblance of urgency. Health conditions which need to be thought of as 'out of the ordinary' have become ordinary. We've learned to live with rampant stress, and it's taking its toll every which way.

But it is not normal

Once the perceived threat has passed or been handled and we're feeling safe, then our physiology and psychology should return to normal without any long-lasting negative effects; our relaxation response, the 'rest and digest' state, ought to kick in, signalling our hormones to 'stand down' so we can return to our baseline states.

Cue a huge intake of breath as we revel in this, our safe-and-soundness. It's within this relaxed state that we can set about replenishing, and it's that topping-back-up which prevents stress from becoming perilous.

We're not built for, nor meant to, handle stress in more than short, sharp bursts, as and when it's truly required. In ancestral days long gone, the stressors would have always been immediate and life-threatening. As hunter-gatherers, dangers such as a woolly mammoth, a hulking tiger, a lack of food, avoiding disease were what we had to contend with. The danger was always quite clear and an isolated instance. Whilst the dangers we must contend with today have changed, our body's responses to stressful situations – of which there are many – have not.

This means that when we receive a bill we cannot pay, our stress response gets activated. When our job is a demanding one, our stress response gets activated. When someone runs a red light and we must swerve to safety, our stress response is activated. When we receive an undesired diagnosis from our doctor, our stress response is activated. Our lives are rife with endless potential perceived stressors, barely giving a chance for our 'rest and digest' states to kick in.

Experiencing stress frequently, relentlessly, and for a prolonged period is the problem, because it can have such a negative impact on our lives and health. This chronic stress doesn't fade away, and it recurrently stems as situational or even anticipatory, rather than being immediate and survival-related, repeatedly creating and recreating the 'fight or flight' response.

There's such a thing as good stress

If we want to slightly oversimplify stress, we can think of it as 'distress', stress that feels negative and bigger than us. Consider that versus 'eustress', the stress which positively affects our state of being and is challenging but manageable.

Eustress is the way we feel when we're excited about something like a birthday party, a date, when we're on holiday or travelling or dancing the waltzers at the fairground (*if* you like them, that is...), or working towards a goal that lights us up. It's those rush of butterflies in your tummy, the skip in your step, the sense of accomplishment, those bright and almost involuntary smiles at the very thought of whatever it is.

There's no feeling of being in danger nor threatened but, as with distress, our physiology alters with a similar rush of hormones and a heightened state as we might when we're experiencing the fight or flight response.

Eustress usually feels mighty good; we feel giddy, happy, exuberant, light, bright, solution-focused, creative, unstoppable, and raring to go. It's a type of stress that's beneficial because it motivates and inspires us to accomplish goals and aspirations. Essentially, it helps us to grow and expand, whereas distress can make us feel shrunken and less than enough or even incapable.

Truthfully, though, we can have too much of even a good thing. Eustress is still a form of stress. And eustress layered with existing chronic stress can feel, ultimately, negative, and overwhelming. Too much of any type of stress does tend to compound and to have an undesired knock-on effect, potentially leading to burnout if not balanced with adequate times of resting and digesting.

Fight and flight aren't the only stress responses

As we've seen, 'flight or fight' is synonymous with stress. We've probably all heard our physiological and behavioural reactions to stress referred to in this way. Interestingly, to flee or to fight are not the only stress responses that we humans can experience.

Another stress response is called 'tend and befriend'. This response is characterised by an instinct to tend to one's own needs, the needs of others and to the needs of children, as well as a desire to 'befriend', to seek out social support which can aid with the coordination of the tending and equally act as a reciprocal defence and reinforcement in times of stress. Where fight or flight is fuelled by adrenaline, it's thought tend and befriend may instead be fuelled by oxytocin.

In addition to fight or flight and tend and befriend, another stress response is called 'freeze'. This response is characterised by a lack of movement or action in the face of stress. It is thought to be a survival mechanism that allows an individual to avoid detection by a predator. We might feel alone, hopeless, disconnected, numb, helpless, stuck, and experience a mind that's gone blank in this state.

Another stress response that has been studied is 'fawn'. This response is characterised by a tendency to comply and please others to avoid conflict or harm. It has been observed in individuals who have experienced chronic stress, abuse, or trauma in their life. Fawning can feel like self-blame, self-sabotage, analysis paralysis, shame, repressing needs, being overly apologetic, disassociating, and trying to blend in.

It is important to note that these different stress responses are not mutually exclusive: an individual may exhibit a combination of these responses depending on the situation and their personal history. Additionally, different people may have a dominant response based on their personality, upbringing, and past experiences.

Stress can even change our menstrual cycles

During the pandemic, an increasing number of conversations about wonky menstrual cycles occurred. I was one of those people who experienced missed periods followed by longer, very heavy periods, with short breaks before another longer, heavy period. In other words, my menstrual cycle was all over the place, and it started going askew in April of 2020, only about a month after lockdown began. Once the schools returned as normal here in Cornwall in September of 2020, my body started getting back into a cycle of sorts. As time has progressed, there have been road bumps during particularly stressful times, but for the most part, my period is back to cycling as it always did.

What I learned (and totally wish I'd always known) was that menstrual cycles are the *best* indicator of women's overall health, and it's not normal for them to go awry unless one is edging towards perimenopause and menopause (which are themselves completely normal processes). Why are we not taught that?! Apparently, it's the steady flow of hormones which are released into our bodies when we're stressed for a prolonged period which interrupt and disrupt our menstrual cycles. And although it's true that, in my late thirties, I had possibly been heading towards those normal cessations of my periods, something about that diagnosis from well-meaning friends and family just felt 'off' to me.

Here are some changes that we might notice if under a lot of stress, or, as a *symptom* of stress:

- We might skip a period altogether or it might be delayed.
- Our periods could arrive earlier than anticipated.
- The cycle might be irregular and all over the place.
- Periods might be more painful or have a different flow than usual.
- Premenstrual Syndrome (PMS) might be worse than what's normal for you.

We store stress in the body

We've all heard the term 'bottled up' used to describe when someone might suppress, mask, or refrain from showing their feelings. It turns out that we can literally bottle up our emotions by storing them within our bodies.

Think of some of the common phrases where we use the body to describe how we are feeling:

- 'That so-and-so is such a pain in the neck.'
- 'I'm fed-up to the back teeth with it.'
- 'I feel sick to my stomach.'
- 'I'm getting cold feet.'
- 'I feel as though I'm carrying the weight of the world on my shoulders.'
- 'I've got a gut feeling that…'
- 'My heart just skipped a beat.'

Consider the tension you feel after a prolonged period of stress: the aches and pains, the knots, the clenched jaw, the grinding of teeth, the migraines, the digestive issues, the nausea, and the tight neck and shoulders. Our bodies clench up and get stuck that way. That's stored stress or emotional information, and it can be stored everywhere; in our tissues, organs, skin, and muscles.

There's a more common understanding now that there is not physical health and mental health, separately, but that they're intrinsically linked and inseparable, undeniably so. And that's why chronic stress is so awful, why it affects everything about us, making us generally unwell. Remember, the stress response is designed for short, sharp bursts. The effect on us when that stress response is constantly cruising is a detrimental one.

How the nervous system works

Within our bodies, we each have a nervous system. It's like a messenger system that runs within the body, between the brain, the spinal cord, and our nerves, which then controls all the body's functions, thoughts, and actions, automatically and unconsciously. It's the foundation of all that we do and feel.

When our nervous system is hyperaroused, that's when we feel restless, impatient, irritable, impulsive, overwhelmed and experience racing thoughts. On the flipside, when our nervous system is hypoaroused, we feel listless, lethargic, exhausted, apathetic, stuck, and experience a foggy brain. The ventral state is right in the middle of the two. It occurs when we feel stable, more resilient to stress and change, anchored, equipped to handle what's on our plates, when we can creatively solve problems and find ways to overcome obstacles.

There are two components to the nervous system: the sympathetic nervous system and the parasympathetic nervous system. These are like the opposite sides of the same coin as they often have opposing effects.

The sympathetic nervous system is commonly known as

the 'fight or flight' response. When we perceive an external threat, this system is activated to help us survive it with quick responses.

The parasympathetic nervous system is commonly known as the 'rest and digest' state and is the state we'd want to be in for most of the time, or until a stressor presents itself. It controls our ability to relax and is the feeling of calm, peace, and safety, a place where we function optimally, physiologically. Approximately 75 to 80 per cent of the nerves within the parasympathetic nervous system are the vagal nerves, also known as the vagus nerve. A cranial nerve, the longest of the 12 cranial nerves, carries information and supplies nerves throughout the body from the gut to the brain.

How to hack the nervous system

We can't learn about stress and how to manage stress without talking a bit more about the vagus nerve, because it has a particularly strong influence over the 'rest and digest' state. When activated, this nerve acts like a powerful brake pedal on the sympathetic nervous system.

Luckily, there are ways we can stimulate the vagus nerve to help us ease back into 'rest and digest', thereby decreasing heart rate, inflammation, and respiration rate whilst increasing digestion, memory consolidation, feelings of calm, and the quality of our sleep. You might:

- paint the roof of your mouth with your tongue;
- hum or gargle;
- laugh;
- move or stretch;
- focus on deep breaths;
- expose yourself to cold (for example, place your hands under cold running water);
- meditate;

- stroke your face, neck, and scalp;
- correct your posture by straightening your spine, pulling your shoulders back, and lifting your head;
- get a massage;
- receive red light therapy; or
- eat bitter herbs (bitters) like dandelion and rocket.

Stress causes damage that can be deadly

Once I dived into learning more about stress so that I could get a better handle on it, I was upset and shocked to learn about the (sometimes irreversible) consequences of chronic stress on our minds and bodies. The topic of stress is interwoven in so many of our conversations that I think we lose sight of the damage it can cause or aren't made aware of this information in a way that could literally save lives.

Studies have shown that in the short-term, stress gives our immune system a boost. When our stress response becomes dysregulated or malfunctions, however, the frightening problems start.

Stress has been linked to skin problems, breakouts, acne, and itchy rashes. As well as affecting our libido, stress can suppress our reproductive systems, impeding our likelihood of becoming pregnant. It wreaks havoc with our digestive systems, and we might experience urinating more frequently, or we may get constipated or have diarrhoea. Our general metabolism can also be affected. Stress is a key contributor in the acceleration of ageing and diabetes and in the development of irritable bowel syndrome (IBS), and is also a prime component in the aggravation of its symptoms.

As well as adversely affecting our quality of life in these ways, *chronic stress also shortens our life expectancy*, because it:

- suppresses our immune system and makes us more susceptible to colds, the flu, and other bacterial and viral infections;
- increases our risks of becoming unwell with heart disease, heart attack, high blood pressure, high cholesterol, stroke, and cancer;
- increases the risk of mental health problems such as depression, anxiety, personality disorders and post-traumatic stress disorder; and
- poses the greatest risk factor in alcohol and drug abuse and addiction.

All the symptoms of stress

When we think of someone as stressed, it's kind of like one of those cartoon characters with steam coming out of their ears and their hair standing on end, looking a little frazzled. Whilst we might certainly feel frazzled and as though we have steam coming out of our ears when we're experiencing stress, there are many more symptoms of stress; it literally affects our whole being and our behaviour in many ways:

- irritability, increasingly frustrated, impatient, and short-tempered;
- feeling overwhelmed, as though there's too much on our plate;
- racing thoughts which feel relentless;
- loss of enjoyment in things we previously relished;
- finding it hard to connect with others;
- difficulty making decisions, remembering things, and focusing on anything;
- procrastination;
- tensed-up, hunched-up, clenched-up;

- feeling jittery, dizzy, or faint;
- prevalent sadness, guilt, shame, worry, hopelessness, and helplessness;
- loneliness and aloneness;
- feeling tearful;
- shortness of breath;
- blurred eyesight;
- wired and tired at bedtime;
- struggling to fall asleep or stay asleep;
- fatigue and sleepiness during the day;
- headaches and/or migraines more often than normal;
- high blood pressure;
- racing or irregular heartbeat;
- aches and pains, including chest pains;
- indigestion, heartburn, or feeling nauseous;
- appetite and weight changes;
- skin changes: acne, rashes, or itchy skin;
- sweating, sometimes excessively, or feeling cold suddenly;
- changes to one's periods or menstrual cycle;
- less interest in sex; and
- exacerbated symptoms of any existing physical or mental health issues.

The red flags

Our bodies are continually communicating with us so that we will take action. We know the cues that tell us when we need the loo, when we're thirsty, and when we're hungry. We acknowledge the pain we feel when we stub our toes, get sunburnt, or get a grazed knee.

We don't always take note, but our bodies also present us with signs that stress has become unmanageable. These are the red flags:

- Tolerance levels take a dip, making us more easily irritated, impatient, angry, and frustrated by things which wouldn't have ordinarily bothered us.
- Everything feels too much; we don't feel equipped for the day ahead and every task feels too demanding.
- Vegging out more than normal; eating more crisps and chocolate, not having the energy to prepare meals, or eating more takeaways.
- No motivation nor energy for anything; wanting to stay in bed, falling into 'scroll-holes', procrastinating

more, as household chores start building up and personal hygiene falls by the wayside.

- Crying more readily at the drop of a hat.
- A heavy feeling on your chest or in the pit of the stomach.
- Disassociating and feeling disconnected from life and those around us.
- Retreating; withdrawing and isolating away from any social interactions.
- Being hypercritical of ourselves and possibly those around us, as though seeing the world through a grey, foggy lens.

Stress and anxiety are not the same thing

Many of the emotional and physical symptoms of stress and anxiety are the same and quite often they're used interchangeably because, they're so similar and hard to tell apart that they're like identical twins. In fact, when trying to describe the sensation of stress, we are also describing the sensation of anxiety.

Medically, the term 'stress' per se is used to describe *acute* stress: that bolt of stress we experience for a short period of time until the threat has been adequately dealt with. It's also the gearing up in preparation to handle something that's arisen or is just coming up. Stress typically has an external stressor, some specific external factor that acts as a trigger to activate the stress response. When we're stressed, we usually know what has caused us to be stressed, we can identify the reasons.

Anxiety, however, doesn't *always* have an obviously identifiable trigger, and the trigger is typically internal, generated by excessive thoughts, rather than external, although stress, too, *can* trigger anxiety. If, once the external stressor has passed, we're still experiencing distress, overthinking, self-judgement, rumination, and overwhelm, then that's more likely anxiety. When we're feeling relenting apprehension and worry about something that's not yet happened, about things that might occur, then there's usually anxiety present as well.

Stress is contagious

One of the most surprising things about stress is that it can be contagious. That is, the stress of one person can spread to others and affect them in the same way. Researchers call this 'emotional contagion'. Emotional contagion occurs when, automatically and without conscious effort, we respond to and adopt the behaviours, posture, and expressions of those around us. As a social species, there's a harmonisation, a tuning-in, that occurs when we're with others.

You've probably noticed emotional contagion, how you might feel differently after spending time with various people, even feeling differently than you did before you saw them. That's because we're impacted by the emotions of the people we spend time with. We're affected even if we don't have a particularly close relationship with someone. For example, if we are in an exchange with someone who is stressed, we may find ourselves becoming more stressed and tense, even if we don't know why.

An extremely controversial study was carried out in 2014, using Facebook to see if emotions are contagious online. It turns out that they are. The researchers influenced the feeds of 700,000 Facebook users with negative content. Those users then went on to share more negative content themselves. What's so interesting about this study is that, with the advent of an increasing amount of people working from home, stress is still contagious even within remote-working environments; those who use apps like Slack, for example, can still 'catch' stress from colleagues without being in the same physical vicinity. Even human–bot interactions can transfer emotions!

Those of us with pets have experienced their knowingness of when we're not okay: the reassuring and comforting nudging, the extra cuddles, or the silent presence as they lay beside us. It won't come as a surprise to learn that the reverse is also common. A Swedish study showed that the stress we're experiencing can be passed on, through emotional contagion, to dogs, causing them to become stressed. In fact, studies have shown that emotional contagion is possible with lots of animals, particularly those who live in groups.

Our perspective makes a difference

Perspective is the way we see things and interpret them. It's the angle, viewpoint, vantage from where we are and where we've come from, influencing how we see, encounter, and understand the world around us. If we have a fixed mindset, we might only be able to look at things in a certain limited way, whereas those with a growth mindset can see contrasting perspectives. But it's also more than that, as our perspectives can be affected by our current emotional states, our current state of mind, our upbringing, our life experience, our personalities, the people we hang out with, our values, our opinions, and our assumptions. All those factors combined, then, create a lens through which we filter and comprehend life's goings on.

It's *such* an advantage to have the capacity to hold more than one perspective at a time. This ability is a decision-making tool but also a crucial component in how we might build (or destroy) relationships. Trying on diverse perspectives for size helps us to weigh risks and rewards, empathise, understand a problem from several different angles; it affords the ability to zoom in and zoom out of issues and consider our approach.

Perspective accounts for *some* of the differentials in whether certain situations are stressful for some and not others. It's all relative, but the meaning we apply to the event also alters the light it's cast in, that is, how much control over the event we believe we have. The perception of something being more than we can handle is typically when something becomes a stressor for someone. This can narrow our outlook, causing distress and all those symptoms like a foggy head. Adopting a perspective that's more in favour of us rather than the event allows us to approach the possible stressor with a more can-do attitude, thereby feeling confident and creatively coming up with solutions in a calm and steady way.

That's not to say we can always think our way out of stress. But when we can – and it makes sense to – override the desire for fight or flight by using grounding techniques to open mental and physical space, then we can often see the situation in a different light.

We all have different stress thresholds

In the same way we have heard of pain thresholds and the way our tolerance for pain varies from person to person, we all have differing stress thresholds. This explains why a stressor for someone else mightn't be a stressor for you, and vice versa. It also depends upon what other stressors someone might already be dealing with. A threshold is the tipping point where something starts to have an adverse effect, the fine line between something feeling manageable and unmanageable.

The expression 'the straw that broke the camel's back' always springs to mind when we talk about stress thresholds. They're our limits, which are individual to each of us and the circumstances of our lives. You can load a fair load of straw onto a camel's back but at some point, it'll be too much. The moment before that last bit, all will seem cope-with-able but there's a whisker of a straw which will set the balance in the opposite direction, causing the camel to collapse under the strain.

We see this play out in our lives too, right? Maybe we're moving house at the same time as we're navigating a work deadline. We're coping, we're managing, until something else happens: a flat tire, a stubbed toe, spilled coffee, and that extra thing that we'd ordinarily cope with so very easily, becomes the final straw, the catalyst where patience just runs dry and brings on an avalanche of big feelings. In other words, it's the point when we've just had enough. It's the very last thing in a line of unsatisfactory events which tips us over the edge from coping to yielding beneath the brawn of it all.

Our threshold for stress is a fluid thing, depending on whether our basic needs are being met, our history and if that includes trauma, how we've seen our parents handle stress, and our health in general. Because our thresholds aren't fixed, they're also expandable. Some things we can do to widen it so we cope and react to stress in less detrimental ways, things like therapy, meditation, self-awareness, emotional intelligence, and physical activity.

When others are stressed about something that you don't perceive to be stressful, never diminish their experience or downplay it. You probably don't have the full picture or an understanding of the life experiences which have brought them to this point. If they're stressed, then they're seeing the situation as being too much.

What stress can look like in others

As friends, parents, teammates, leaders, and whatever role we hold, it's important to understand the signs that someone might be stressed so that we can lean in to help.

One note about leaning in: so often we express our empathy and follow-up by saying, 'Please let me know if there's anything I can do.' That puts the onus on someone who is already feeling depleted, unsure, among all else, to think, to be decisive and to ask. So, don't do that. Instead, *be proactive, not reactive*. Ask them how they *really* are and listen to their response, properly listen, and don't offer unsolicited advice. Invite their kids to yours for a playdate or a sleepover or make a set of meals for their freezer. Invite them on a walk away from their work desk, look at their workload, and say you're happy to take XYZ off their hands. If you know them well and are often at their house, help with laundry, dishes, and other household stuff and give them space to take a break. You'll know your person better than I do, so you're best placed to know what they'd value. But do, *do*. Share their burdens with them, lighten the load they're carrying, and help make space for rest.

So, back onto what it might look like when someone is stressed:

- rapid or slower than normal speech;
- listless or restless;
- furrowed brow, hunched and tense;
- biting their nails, clenching their jaw, or grinding their teeth;
- clumsiness, forgetfulness, and impatience;
- significant mood and appearance changes; they feel, sound, and look different;
- lack of personal hygiene;
- absence from work or social activities;
- overreacting, angrier than usual and/or more tearful;
- self-isolating;
- contracted posture;
- hypervigilance;
- quieter than usual, or louder, less inhibited, than usual; or
- expressing how pointless, useless, or hopeless they feel or think things are.

And, of course, they might be wearing a big beaming smile because some people are able to mask their feelings all too well. Just because someone looks bright and breezy doesn't mean that they are. People often suffer in silence and alone for fear of being a burden. In this case, you mightn't suspect anything out of the ordinary but do give people the benefit of the doubt if they're slow to respond to texts or cancel plans. Let's be kind to ourselves and one another. Better to be kind than sorry.

Stress erodes our capacity for empathy

Empathy is the psychological and emotional understanding, awareness, and feeling of what someone else is experiencing. It's being able to imagine standing in someone else's shoes and to see things from their perspective, or the ability to live vicariously, seeing and feeling their emotions even if your circumstances differ. Empathy is a linchpin to how we relate with and to others, a key consideration in design thinking, engineering, marketing, and product development, and a crucial skill we'd like all our leaders to embody.

When we experience empathy, we feel seen, heard, and understood.

Short-term stress affects the brain's ability to regulate emotions and process social cues which makes relating and communicating with others more difficult, but once the stressful episode is over, the functions return to normal. Chronic stress, however, well... that's a different story. Chronic stress has the propensity to cause inflammation in the brain and to alter the way our brain functions, and it impairs the way the neurons communicate with one another, longer-term.

If our capacity to process social cues and regulate our emotions are diminished under stress even in the short term, then empathy, which is the ability to process them and feel them will also be diminished. Additionally, we need to factor in the physical and mental exertion and exhaustion that stress causes, depleting us of energy, which also makes empathy more difficult.

It's such a vicious cycle, because the increase in stress levels coinciding with a decrease in our capacity for empathy causes us to feel isolated, alone, and disconnected from others (a stressor in itself).

Stress affects our executive functioning

Our executive function is a set of cognitive functions which help us stay on top of things, such as focusing, planning, prioritising, assimilating, filtering, organising, remembering, completing tasks, and managing our time, emotions, and impulses. These functions are controlled by the part of our brain called the frontal lobe and they help us to cope with a multitude of responsibilities and commitments. It's thanks to these functions that we're able to attain our goals.

Stress plays havoc with our executive functions. It's thought that when our stress response is activated, the executive function resources are reallocated elsewhere for the stressor to be dealt with. This is all fine and dandy with those short sharp bursts of stress, but where chronic stress is concerned, the impact of this leads to widespread disarray.

When our executive function gets impaired, we might find it difficult to sustain effort, to focus and concentrate, reading a page several times but not taking in any of the information. Any tasks that require mental juice and attention to detail might feel a bit beyond our capabilities. Our ability to retain information and dates will be compromised. Making decisions is affected because we find it harder to weigh up risks and rewards and to make rational, unemotionally reactive choices. Our tolerance levels decrease too, making us more easily frustrated, irritated, and sensitive to criticism. Our emotions may feel more intense. In a nutshell, our lives could feel turned upside down and inside out as we struggle to prioritise, organise, plan, and cope under the influence of chronic stress.

Stress can become a habit

Anything we do repeatedly becomes a habit; it's how habits are built and ingrained. We're habitual folk with up to 95 per cent of our thoughts and behaviours being habitual ones; we naturally like to create routines, look for patterns, and stick with what's comfortable and familiar.

In our brains, we have these things called neural pathways, the connections between the neurons. These connections form based on our habits and behaviours, making those habits and behaviours more and more automatic over time. It's like going for a walk on a path that's been travelled many times by many people, until it's a clear and direct pathway, rather than a wild one where you're having to duck and dive beneath branches and watch your footing. That clear and direct path is well established. And that's what happens to our neural pathways when, over time, a set of behaviours becomes a habit.

In contrast, new habits are difficult to build, because you're trying to create a new pathway and your brain wants to take the easy, existing, efficient, established route. Once a new pathway is entrenched after repeatedly doing the same behaviours it's literally locked in until you decide to change it.

Because so much of what we do is habitual, it's fair to say that some of those habits mightn't be serving us, or that they might be causing us stress. If we tell ourselves we work best when we work under pressure and then something happens to throw us off track, then we've actively created a highly stressed and unpredictable environment for ourselves.

I used to do this all the time, procrastinating until the last moment and then pulling out all the stops to meet the deadline. It *seemed* to be the only way I could meet deadlines and prioritise my work. Most of the time, something would crop up (as it so often does in life), throwing me into disarray, meaning I'd have to compromise all my healthy habits (like the conditions I'd set up to ensure a good night's sleep), forgoing exercise, and, reluctantly, spending less time with my family to get my work done on time. In truth, it was a habit I'd created over time and one which was having a negative impact on me and those around me.

People-pleasing is another habit that causes a great deal of untold stress. Overscheduling, struggling to say 'No', avoiding or numbing our feelings, emotional eating, binging on information, not communicating or renegotiating boundaries, complaining a lot, adopting a fixed mindset, using not-so-nice self-talk, running on empty, and procrastinating are some examples of other habits which can cause stress.

What we consume can aggravate stress

We've all watched a scary movie and felt our hearts race at the jump-scare parts. Perhaps we've cried while watching the news, horrified at the scenes we're seeing. Or we've *really* got into a sports game. Or we've been aroused by words in a steamy romance novel, or swept up and away or calmed by the beats of music, or cried with laughter at a funny TikTok.

Similarly, if we're surrounded by people who veer onto the negative side of life, we struggle against becoming negative ourselves. Same goes for spending time with those of a sunnier disposition when we might even struggle to *not* feel sunny ourselves!

These things which are all external, can become internal, impacting our emotional, mental, and physical states.

We notice how the different foods and drinks we consume can change how we feel in ourselves and impact our thoughts; we talk of carb comas, handovers, and the sugar shakes when we've overindulged in some food groups. Too much caffeine and we get the jitters and might find ourselves feeling hypervigilant and anxious.

Stress can affect our appetite and have us reaching for so-called comfort foods – sweet, salty, fatty foods, like pizza, ice cream, crisps, donuts, chocolate, and fries. But those foods themselves can also cause stress within the body in a few different ways. Some foods are so nutrient sparse that they don't give us the fuel we need to operate properly. Eating lots of those foods can cause nutrient deficits within the body. Foods which increase our blood sugar levels create problems as well, because our body then needs to regulate those levels which it does by releasing insulin into the blood which can lead to the release of cortisol too. Caffeine, sugar, and alcohol can decrease the quality of our sleep, thereby creating a knock-on effect, because sleep plays an important role in how we manage stress.

What we consume, we become. Everything we take in, the food and beverages we eat and drink, the ingredients in the products we use to clean and buff our faces and homes, even what we see and hear on the television, in books, and on social media – all those elements alter and influence who we are, what we are, and how we are.

Stress and resilience are intertwined

Resilience refers to the process of positive adaptation when confronted with challenges, adversity, trauma, and tragedy. It's our 'bouncebackability', how we hold up against, recover, react, and approach those situations to get through and overcome them. Typically, resilient people are solution-focused during difficult times, rather than getting caught up in directing their energies and attention toward the problem itself.

The best bit about resilience is it's like a muscle: the more we flex it, the stronger it gets. It's something we can build upon and choose to get better at with practice. Mindset plays a role in our resilience; how confident we are, how much self-esteem we possess, how self-aware we are, whether we typically adopt a positive approach to setbacks, and our level of tenacity. Support systems help foster resilience too, and having those to lean on, to be bolstered and encouraged by, helps hugely.

Resilient people still experience stress but what sets them apart from someone who mightn't be as resilient is their capability in managing that stress to reduce the negative impact on their lives. They retain the healthy habits they established, knowing that those habits can increase their resilience (things like good sleep hygiene, the healthy coping mechanisms for expressing and releasing the stress, for example). Stress counterpoises resilience, because the more resilient we are, the less stress we perceive, just as the more stress we perceive, the less resilient we might be. It's worth noting that during moments when we're being wildly resilient, we don't always recognise our own resilience, our own strength, because it's being put to the test.

The concept of the stress bucket

The stress bucket is a visual concept that refers to the amount of stress an individual can handle before reaching a breaking point. Imagine you have a bucket. It's not the same size as someone else's bucket because everyone has a certain capacity for stress, and this capacity can vary depending on a variety of factors such as overall health, coping mechanisms, and support systems. As you experience stressors, they get added to the bucket. Some might be small stressors, and some might be bigger. When stressors are added to the bucket, they can fill it up; the fuller our 'stress bucket' becomes, the more we might feel overwhelmed and unable to handle additional stress. When the stress bucket is full, and there are no mechanisms to deal with that, that overflow can lead to chronic stress.

The stress bucket concept can clarify how stress affects us individually and in identifying when stress levels are becoming too high. It can also be used as a tool for managing stress by identifying which stressors can be removed or reduced, and finding ways to increase coping mechanisms and support systems, which give the bucket a chance to empty again.

Regularly monitoring and managing stress in this way can help to keep the stress bucket from overflowing and prevent negative effects on our health.

The stress bucket is not a fixed entity either. People can change the size of their bucket, by learning new coping strategies, and building resilience.

For me, learning about the stress bucket was a game-changer. My perspective on stress changed but perhaps, more importantly, I stopped shaming myself for not being able to cope with a constantly overflowing bucket. Instead, I started seeing my life through a different lens which felt, for want of a better word, empowering: rather than be the victim of these stressful things, I could do something about them.

What helped significantly was taking note of what things increased my capacity to handle stress and what decreased it, as well as how those things felt, what they were, and the circumstances surrounding them, while always being mindful of what I could do to tip the balance in my favour. If a day ahead looked particularly burdensome, then I'd consider how my rest and reprieve from the weight of that could be comparable or exceed those burdens I'd need to handle.

Spoon theory

You may have read or heard of people referring to themselves as 'spoonies'. These are people who live with chronic illness and who are referring to the spoon theory. It's a theory synonymous with disability or chronic illness – which is just what chronic stress is.

This brilliant theory was created by Christine Miserandino, who used it as a metaphor to describe how she coped with the effects of lupus (an autoimmune disorder). Christine used spoons to illustrate how chronic illness limited her energy and the resources available for daily life.

We all have spoons at our disposal at the beginning of each day. The number of spoons we have available will depend upon varying factors and conditions of our environment, how much sleep we might've had, pain levels, medication, etc. For example, let's say you start the day with 20 spoons, representing the amount of physical, emotional, and mental energy you have available for the coming day. Anything you do uses a spoon. (For me, tasks like brushing my teeth, making my bed, making, or taking phone calls, replying to emails and social media comments and messages, and any kind of socialising tend to take up *way* more spoons than things like reading, going for a walk, or anything creative.) With only 20 spoons to start with, we must get nifty at prioritising and choosing where our spoons will be used.

Even the constant decision-making and balancing of resources takes spoons. The seemingly small tasks to someone who is healthy and well might be a Herculean task for someone who isn't, taking more spoons than we might imagine. Those who have had to use spoons on necessary and important tasks might then need to cancel plans, become reluctant to make future commitments, and need to renegotiate expectations.

Some people talk of 'borrowing spoons' from tomorrow; however, because the number of spoons available on any given day is uncertain and unpredictable, and because nobody knows how much sleep they might get, what their pain levels might be, what other factors could crop up, using tomorrow's spoons when you don't know how many spoons you might wake up with, can lead to complete depletion of resources too early in the day. The result: you mightn't have enough to cope with what that day might require.

Learning of the spoon theory many moons ago when I was living with debilitating depression helped me to zoom out of moments in my days and to consider the impact that today's 'asks' or demands might have on me tomorrow. It was mighty helpful in changing the way I communicate my needs, resources, and energy (or lack thereof) to other people. Even nowadays, I still think of my day in terms of spoons and when I'm planning my time. I make sure that I limit the number of meetings and phone calls I might have in any given week. I batch-reply to emails and social media in a set period rather than try to do so as and when they pop-up. Maximising the quality of sleep is also a priority because this is the biggest factor in providing me with more spoons each day. Thinking of our resources as finite is a good strategy when balancing the demands placed on us.

The notion of stress cycles

Developed by Drs. Emily and Amelia Nagoski, I first heard about the 'stress cycle' from their book: *Burnout: The Secret to Solving the Stress Cycle*. In their book, they describe the physiological response of the body to stress and how it consists of three stages: the beginning, the middle, and the end, or alarm, resistance, and exhaustion.

The alarm stage occurs when the body experiences a stressor which activates the fight or flight response. During the resistance stage, the body is trying to maintain the response to stress to cope with the stressor. We can sustain this stage for a while, but eventually, it'll undoubtedly lead to the exhaustion stage. In the exhaustion stage, the body has exhausted its resources and is unable to maintain the stress response. Getting stuck in this stage is what leads to negative physical and emotional effects, such as burnout.

But, *if* we can find a way to let our bodies know that we're no longer under attack, threatened or in danger, we can put an end to the stress cycle, moving through it into relaxation and calm. Do this in the right way and you literally feel a shift in your body, the sigh of relief, the release of physical tension or a change in how you feel mentally.

As I was smack-bang in the middle of burnout when I read this book, the way doctors Emily and Amelia Nagoski explained that there are ways you can close these cycles gave me those ever-so-precious glimmers of hope. Rather than lingering, and thereby feeling helpless, I could interrupt the stress signal and signal to my body that I was safe, triggering the rest and digest response. This led me down the merry path of learning about all the ways to do just that, the embodiment of Part Two of this book.

Part Two

Stress literally and metaphorically makes us dizzy. And stuck. As though we're wading through a swamp of sinking sand. The more we plough on to get a grasp on the situation, the more we seem to be sinking. That feeling of being stuck and not knowing how to escape it (or even if you can), is downright terrifying.

It's also all too easy to just accept that this is how things are now and to plod on, head down, just trying to push through. I'm hoping what follows is the needed light at the end of the tunnel, presenting options, ideas, tools, and techniques to help untangle yourself from it all – hope.

In the thick of it

When we're right in the middle of a stress-storm, a sense of hopelessness and helplessness can wash over us. The most self-helpful thing we can do, in that moment, is to take action. Taking action has been proven to lessen the feelings of helplessness which do tend to keep us stuck.

It's important too, that we signal, somehow, to our minds and bodies that *we are safe*, so that the fight and flight response can step down.

If you're in the thick of it, this is the most important part of the book for you, containing lots of ideas for things to do in those moments to bring on a sense of calm. Whether you chuck this book in your bag with this section easily marked and grabbable (a sticky marker that screams, 'Here it is!') or take photos or make notes on your phone and add shortcuts to your home screen, make sure you're tooled-up for the times you need to quickly and easily access these tools.

And breathe...

Becoming aware and in control of your breath is one of the most effective ways to temper the stress and anxiety we feel. As we concentrate on taking slower and deeper breaths, it sends a signal to our nervous system that we're safe and helps it to calm down. You can practise these ahead of time so that they don't feel so strange to you when you need them, and they're best done with a straight upright posture whilst sitting.

Here are five ways to become aware and in control of your breath. Give them a go and see which one works best for you.

Square breathing
Also known as box breathing.

Just as a square has four sides, there are four steps to this exercise, with each step lasting four seconds. Repeat the following steps until you feel a sense of calm wash over you.

1. Breathe in through your nose.
2. Hold your breath.

3. Breathe out.

4. Hold your breath.

I find it helps to have my eyes closed and to imagine I'm drawing a square in my mind as I complete each stage.

Ten-second breath

Also known as equal breathing.

Repeat the following steps ten times each until you feel relaxed.

1. Breathe in through your nose slowly for a count of five and hold the breath for a moment.
2. Breathe out slowly through your nose for a count of five and hold the exhale for a moment.

Alternate nostril

As the name implies, alternate nostril breathing is when we close and block alternate nostrils as we take breaths with the other one and take it in turns over and over. Repeat the following steps until you feel the stress and anxiety wash away.

1. Take a deep breath in and exhale slowly.
2. Push your right nostril closed, using your thumb.
3. Take a breath in through your left nostril.
4. Push your left nostril closed, using the ring finger of

the same hand as the thumb you're using.

5. Remove your thumb from your right nostril and exhale.
6. Take a breath in through your right nostril.
7. Push your right nostril closed, using your thumb.
8. Remove your ring finger from your left nostril and exhale.
9. Take a breath in through your left nostril.
10. Repeat the pattern above.

Four-seven-eight breathing

Place the tip of your tongue against the gum behind and above your front teeth. Remember the numbers 'four', 'seven', and 'eight' as you work through the following steps until you feel re-centred. It'll likely take four rounds:

1. Take a deep breath in, through your nose, as you silently count to four, and *not quickly. Try adding a small beat or pause between each count.*
2. Hold that breath as you silently count to seven.
3. Release the breath as you silently count to eight.

If you feel lightheaded when you practise this breathing technique, try altering the counts to 'two', 'three', and 'five' and instead of 'four', 'seven', and 'eight'.

Cyclic sighing

Set a timer for five minutes, then repeat the following steps until the time is up.

1. Take a deep breath in through your nose.
2. Take a second deeper breath in to fill your lungs as much as you can.
3. Slowly, exhale through your breath until the air is fully gone.

Get grounded

When we feel ruffled, jumpy, distracted, stressed, dissociated, nervous, fatigued, and all a dither, with a head that's spinning, we can think of that as being ungrounded.

There are a few things we can do to soothe our nervous system and bring ourselves back to the present moment. The aforementioned breathing exercises will help with this too, but I thought I'd share some of my favourite alternatives.

Five, four, three, two, one technique

This mindfulness exercise works so well because it takes you out of your head and helps you to focus on your senses and the way you're interacting with the world around you. Take a deep breath in and slowly breathe out, then:

1. name five things you can see;
2. touch four things;
3. name three different sounds you can hear;
4. identify two smells; and
5. think of one thing can you taste.

Positive self-talk

Often referred to as mantras or affirmations, these effective phrases, through repetition, reinforce positive self-talk by replacing the not-so-nice thoughts with more positive and empowering ones. They quieten our minds, reduce stress, bolster confidence, and they help to keep us focused on the present, taking away the power from those horrible mental downward spirals.

Pick any positive phrase that resonates. Here are some that I often turn to.

- This *will* pass.
- It's going to be okay. *I'm* going to be okay.
- I'm safe.
- I've *so, so, so* got this.
- I am doing my best.
- I am capable of amazing things.
- I am worthy of all that's great.
- I am brave, and I can get through this.
- My thoughts are not facts.
- I am tougher than tough times.
- I've done this before, and I can do it again.
- This is overcome-able.
- I'm already bouncing back from this.

Counting

- Choose a number and count in multiples and see how high you can get.
- Count backwards from 100.
- If you're in the car, you could choose to count the number of, say, red cars that you see.
- You could also count people with blue coats or stripy tops on if you're on a train or somewhere busy.

A–Z game

A personal favourite. My family played this game when I was growing up, and so it feels comforting. It's also useful, because if you're with someone who is feeling stressed or anxious, you can do together.

First, choose a topic, any topic; it could be animals, food, drinks, names, countries, cities, or even what you can see. Then work through the alphabet, finding something in that category or topic for each letter.

A for...

B for...

C for...

D for...

And so on.

Embracing nature

Numerous studies attest to the stress-relieving benefits of

being in nature, looking out of our windows or at art or photographs depicting nature. Exposure to nature reduces our levels of stress hormones, lowers our blood pressure, and gives our endorphin and dopamine levels a boost. Harvard University claims that it takes just 20 minutes in nature to feel these benefits. Here are some ways you can tap into them.

- Take a walk outdoors.
- Spend time in the woods or forest.
- Tree-bathe: stand still and look up at the trees.
- Hug a tree (yes, really!).
- Sit next to running water.
- Swim in the sea or go wave-jumping.
- Make a sandcastle.
- Go on a boat trip or kayak or canoe.
- Try skimming rocks.
- Walk barefoot in the grass or mud.
- Roly-poly down a not-too-steep bank.
- Make a mud pie.
- Climb a tree.
- Watch a sunset or sunrise.
- Do some gardening.
- Have a picnic.
- Cartwheel and do handstands in the grass.
- Have a snowball fight.
- Build a snowman.

- Meditate outside.
- Read a book outdoors.
- Birdwatch or plant-watch.
- Listen to the birds.
- Draw or paint a picture that's nature-related.
- Stargaze.
- Make shapes out of the clouds.
- Tend potted plants inside your home.
- Hang a bird feeder in your garden.

Use our common sense(s)

When we're experiencing stress, we can tap into our senses to help send soothing signals to our brains.

Touch
A powerful way we can show others support and express our feelings. Human touch with the right person produces the hormone oxytocin which has been shown to reduce stress and pain. There's also self-supportive touch which has a similar effect, soothing the sympathetic nervous system, making us feel safer, secure, and less alone. Try some of these.

- Hug another human.
- Hug yourself.
- Hold hands with someone.
- Hold your own hands.
- Gently stroke your arm, leg, or hair.
- Place your hand on your heart as you take deep breaths.
- Ask someone else to gently stroke your arm, leg, or hair.
- Massage.

- Snuggle in a blanket.
- Stroke a cat or dog.
- Hold a mug with a hot drink in it.
- Cuddle a hot water bottle or a cuddly toy.
- Wear a comforting piece of clothing.
- Place your hand in cold water.
- Splash your face with cold water.
- Take a warm bath.
- Play with a fidget toy or slime.
- Apply lotion or a lip balm.
- Walk barefoot in the grass or sand.

Smell

Our sense of smell is part of our olfactory system, a rather special system because it is directly connected with the parts of the brain which regulate our emotions, making the sense of smell powerful for relieving stress. Smell, more than any of our other senses, is emotive and most closely linked to our memories. In times of stress, if we can get a whiff of a smell that's familiar to us in a *positive* way, one that can promote healing and relaxation, we can quite quickly feel comforted and calm. Here are some ideas.

- Carry a hankie which has a spray of perfume that our favourite people wear.
- Take a deep breath of fresh air in through your nose.
- Bake a recipe which evokes positive memories.

- Use essential oils, whether in a diffuser or in roller balls for application to your pulse points. Studies have found that some of the most relaxing and comforting scents are lavender, jasmine, sandalwood, bergamot, chamomile, citrus, mango, vanilla, ylang ylang, lemongrass, and rose.
- Light a candle.

Taste

This seems to be the least-researched sense when it comes to relieving stress levels, but there's no doubt that stress can affect the types of foods we might reach for when we feel up against it and how hungry we might or mightn't feel.

Here are some ways we can mindfully use taste to calm and soothe.

- Prepare a drink or meal slowly and intentionally, taking note to be present with the ingredients and stages of the preparation process.
- Drinks like chamomile tea have been proven to have a calming effect.
- Make a food that's associated with a comforting memory or person.
- Eat a handful of berries; they're sweet (so often something we crave when we feel stressed) and also contain vitamin C and antioxidants, which have been shown to help protect the body from stress.

- Other foods which science says help with stress are sweet potatoes, matcha, kimchi, eggs, garlic, turmeric, avocado, pumpkin seeds, and my favourite, dark chocolate.
- Gargling water activates our vocal cords and causes the muscles at the back of our throat to vibrate, both of which stimulates our vagus nerve.

Sight

Stress causes hypervigilance as we zoom in and focus on the cause of stress. Increased levels of adrenaline can cause our vision to go blurry. Or our eyes can get twitchy, they can become dryer, and our pupils will dilate to let in more light. Sustained, this dilation and strain can cause headaches and light sensitivity.

Here are some ways we can use sight to soothe.

- Google 'fractals' and view these natural, repeating patterns; they have been shown to reduce stress levels by a whopping 60 per cent.
- We can close our eyes as we take deep breaths in and out.
- Take a mindful walk and pay attention to the different things you can see.
- Look at photos or watch videos of our favourite people or happy memories.
- Look at photos or watch videos or a livestream of natural settings.

- Look at photos or watch videos or a livestream of cute animals.
- Draw, paint, doodle; do a jigsaw puzzle, a crossword, or a word search.

Sound

We're well acquainted with how stressful some sounds can be, even intentionally so. A crying baby is supposed to be a call to action, a ringing doorbell makes us get up to see who is at the door, and the constant honking of a car horn for a sustained period is super annoying. While increased exposure to unwanted sounds can increase our sensitivity to stress, deliberately playing or listening to sounds which have been scientifically proven to induce a state of relaxation can be helpful when we're in the murky thick of stress.

Here are some suggestions.

- Listen to nature sounds: raindrops, a babbling brook, sea waves ebbing and flowing, birds chirping, trees rustling, etc.
- Put on your favourite music or a calming playlist made specifically for times like these.
- Sing a song, loudly.
- Call a supportive and empathetic friend.
- Listen to a podcast or audiobook.
- Hum a rhythm or chant 'om'.

Proprioception

Also known as kinaesthesia or the body awareness sense, proprioception is how our body knows where it is in relation to all else. It also allows our limbs to move at the right time, with the correct speed, and with the adequate amount of force. Our skin, muscles, and joints act as receptors, stimulated by pressure, thereby connecting the brain and the nervous system.

Here are some activities which use proprioception to help relieve stress.

- Sit or lie beneath a weighted blanket.
- Jump on a trampoline or play hopscotch.
- Do cartwheels, jumping jacks or push-ups.
- Climb a tree.
- Chew gum.
- Blow bubbles.
- Eat crunchy foods.
- Do tai chi, swim, or go for a bike ride.
- Have a massage or massage parts of your body.
- Clean, especially if it's weight-bearing cleaning like lugging a mop or vacuum about.
- Give or receive a tight hug or squeeze.
- Balance on one leg.

Interoception

The feeling of needing to go to the loo, a growling stomach, intuition, or thirst is interoception in action. It's an internal sensory system which makes sense of the sensations, feelings, and information within our bodies, including our emotional state. Recent research has examined the link between interoception and stress. Those who are less aware of their own bodily internal changes and cues have been shown to be less able to cope with stress.

One of the most beneficial ways we can tap into interoception to help us to feel grounded is by doing a body scan:

- Lie down or sit somewhere that feels comfortable.
- Take a few deep breaths in and out; long, slow inhales in through your nose and long, slow exhales out through your mouth.
- Turn your attention to your feet. Notice how they feel; are they hot or cold? If you have socks on, are they warm and comfortable or constricting and uncomfortable? Do your feet feel as though they're holding any fatigue, restlessness, tension, pain, or pressure? Notice, too, any emotions, thoughts or feelings which arise as you focus on your feet. Keep breathing through and into those sensations and emotions, imagining any tension or pain being released as you exhale.
- Work your way up your body from the tips of your toes to the top of your head. Take time to focus in on the different areas and differing sensations, staying with the

tension or pain and breathing through it as a release.

Vestibular

Our vestibular sense of gravity and spatial orientation is monitored by our vestibular system which helps us maintain our balance and posture. The vestibular system is the most connected sensory system in our bodies and plays a vital role in our fine motor skills, co-ordination, and self-regulation. Fun fact: most of the 'sensing' of this sense is done through our inner ear. That's why we can often feel dizzy or unbalanced when we have an inner ear infection.

Activities which might provide a sense of calm and balance include:

- Swinging on a swing or hammock.
- Doing handstands.
- Sitting on a gym ball.
- Doing yoga.
- Sitting in a rocking chair as it rocks back and forth.
- Walking on a balance beam.
- Hanging your head off the side of your bed.
- Skipping.
- Playing Twister.
- Ride a bike, rollerblade, or roller skates.
- Singing songs with actions like 'The Time Warp' or 'The Macarena'.

Somatic practices

Derived from the Greek word *soma,* which means body, the term 'somatics' refers to the mindfulness, awareness, sensitivity, and presence within the moments of movement. Encompassing proprioception, interoception, and exteroception (the external environment), somatic practices focus on the experience and feelings of our bodies, rather than fitting to form as so many stretching or weight-lifting exercises so often do.

The approach is a gentle one, grounded in stillness and softness. Through feeling and tuning in to the body, we're able to isolate exactly where tension is held and work to contract and release the tension, stress, and trauma, and increasing mobility at those exact spots. By paying attention to how we feel, we can more quickly spot discomfort, say, in our neck, and then use somatics to ease that discomfort.

Try it: Whilst it's often recommended to work with a trained therapist, particularly as it can help relive pent-up trauma, group classes are available including some online. If you'd like to learn more, a wealth of YouTube videos is available.

Tapping

Before reading further, if you're going through times which are extraordinarily tough, intense, and traumatic, have done so in the past, or have a diagnosed mental health condition, I'd strongly encourage you to seek the support of an Emotional Freedom Technique (EFT) practitioner before you try tapping at home, so that you are supported and safe.

It has been clinically proven that tapping or, as it's also known, 'Emotional Freedom Technique (EFT)' can relieve stress, anxiety, and pain by 40 per cent in just minutes. Tapping on certain pressure points on the body has been shown to send a signal to the amygdala in the brain that we're safe, in turn, shutting down the stress response, and releasing stuck energy and emotion from the body.

There are more than 360 acupressure points in the body and tapping tends to centre on these nine:

* the side of the hand (hold your hand out in a karate chop pose and it's the underside of your hand, not the

palm or top of your hand, but the underside along from your little finger);

- the crown of your head;
- just above the eyebrows;
- to the side of your eyes;
- just under your eyes, the tops of the apples of your cheeks;
- under the nose, the indent that runs from your nose to your top lip;
- under the mouth, the indent just above your chin;
- under your collarbone, to the centre;
- under the arm, just under the armpit;

The basis of the technique is to identify the feeling of discomfort, whether that be stress, a jolt of nerves, a craving, pain, or a negative thought, and then rate the intensity of the feeling out of ten. The next step is to systematically tap each of the above acupressure points in turn. As you do so, you can say phrases aloud like, 'Even though I feel [insert the feeling here: anxious, scared, stressed, etc.], I deeply and completely accept myself.' In as little as five minutes, you should notice that your heart rate has settled, your breathing is more relaxed, and the original score out of ten has decreased.

Try it: YouTube has a plethora of videos, which I highly recommend because you can search for terms like 'EFT for stress', or 'EFT for pain relief' and be guided through the process.

Autonomous sensory meridian response (ASMR)

Autonomous sensory meridian response (ASMR) videos have taken the online world by storm in recent years, but it's not easy to describe this response, which some call 'brain tingles' or 'braingasms'. You know that feeling when the someone whispers, and you get tingly goosebumps that travel from your scalp and down your neck to your spine? That's ASMR: a tingling, calming, and sometimes referred to by the term 'euphoric sensation'.

The response is triggered by audio, visual, and tactile stimuli and best described as deeply relaxing, meditative, and comforting. Humming, typing, rustling leaves, steady rain, soft repetitive movements, getting a haircut or massage, page-turning, lava lamps, cooking sounds, hair brushing, tapping on objects, or hearing ocean waves, for example, are some of the common ASMR triggers.

Whilst there's not a huge amount of research yet – that's bound to follow – there are early suggestions that not everyone experiences ASMR. What's promising out of this early research are the health benefits of ASMR: lower heart rate; reduced stress, anxiety, and pain; improved sleep; aided ability to fall asleep; and increases in positive mood.

Try it: Head to TikTok, YouTube, or Spotify and search for 'ASMR'.

The aftermath

After a stressful event, we can sometimes experience an emotional hangover; feeling groggy, low, exhausted, lethargic, drained, despondent, tearful, replaying the situation over and over, re-feeling the feelings, and careening between a general emptiness or everything's-too-much-ness.

The very act of suppressing our emotions has been shown to make matters worse, leading to increased stress levels and elevated blood pressure. Turns out, a problem shared might well be a problem halved, after all. According to Professor Matthew Lieberman, Professor and Social Cognitive Neuroscience Lab Director at The University of California, Los Angeles, when we describe an emotion, it diminishes the feeling of it. This decrease is visible in an MRI scan, which shows the level of activity in the amygdala decreased. In other words, when we speak about our emotions, we feel less stressed. And as you've seen, this part of the book is focused on ways we can express and process the stress.

Shake it off

You may have heard of therapeutic tremoring, neurogenic tremoring, shaking therapy, somatic shaking, or meditative shaking to shake off stress and regulate the nervous system. Shaking is a natural and often involuntary reaction to extreme stress and fear. We see it in the wild when animals have been chased by predators and have managed to escape or when our pet dogs have been frightened like after a trip to the vet; they instinctively shake to discharge the tension, energy, and trauma of the stressful situation. These shakes reduce activity in our neuroendocrine system, which is responsible for regulating the stress hormones, our emotions, and our energy levels.

Try it: In the aftermath of a stressful time, shake your limbs. You could work clockwise around your body, starting with your left arm, followed by your left leg, right leg, right arm, and then your whole self. This will release any tension in your body, burn off that excess adrenaline and calm your nervous system.

Stretch it out

Our stress response is driven by the *sympathetic* nervous system. Our *parasympathetic* nervous system is responsible for relaxing your body after the threat or danger has passed. Stretching slows down the production of stress hormones and activates the parasympathetic nervous system. It also helps circulate oxygen around the body, increases blood flow, and helps to release tension we might be holding onto.

Try it: Head to YouTube and search for 'stretching exercises to help with stress'. There are quite literally thousands of videos you can follow along with.

Dance it out

Dancing, like any physical movement, helps the body to release endorphins and serotonin which are the hormones which help us to feel good. It's impossible to feel stressed *and* feel good so anything we do that releases endorphins will help to relieve the stress we feel. As you're dancing, you're focusing on the music and expressing yourself, creatively, which can elevate your mood, stretch out those limbs and muscles, and it's often a whole heap of fun too.

Try it: Pop on a song and dance as though nobody is watching. Absolutely go for it! Feel the beat and move to the music.

Talk it out

Bottling up our feelings and suppressing our emotions is thought to cause physical stress on the body. Avoiding confrontation, not wanting to be accused of attention seeking or of being a 'snowflake', downplaying the impact something or someone has had on us, or holding in sadness, fear, anger, and frustration – those are the emotions society deems as 'less desirable', right? So, we supress them. In contrast, we don't tend to feel as though we should hold in happiness, joy, excitement, or bravery.

Whilst talking about our feelings with someone we trust is cathartic it's also dipping into social support which helps stave away loneliness, releases the pressure we're feeling, and opens the door for us to get help. Putting our feelings into words is a process that can be really healing.

Try it: Talk with someone you trust, such as a friend, family member, teacher, colleague, or therapist.

Cry it out

Since the day we were born, crying has been a way to express our feelings. As we get older and learn to talk and express ourselves in other ways, we cry less than we did when we were newborn babies. Still, there's no denying the sense of release that can come with a good cry. Scientists have said that when we cry, we release oxytocin and endorphins which sooth emotional and physical pain. Their research also shows that crying activates the parasympathetic nervous system, thus helping us to feel more relaxed and soothed. According to the American Academy of Ophthalmology, when we emotionally cry, as opposed to secreting reflex tears and basal tears, our tears contain stress hormones. 'Better out than in' has never been truer.

Try it: If you feel the onset of tears, let them fall. Don't try to prevent yourself from crying.

Write it out

A fantastic way to release and express stress is to write about it. Journaling is said to reduce our self-judgement, help us to accept and regulate our emotions, and increase our awareness and understanding of our needs. The act of putting our thoughts down onto paper feels cathartic, as though we're unburdening ourselves in a way that's beneficial to our wellbeing.

In fact, one of the workshops I host is a guided journaling session called Express the Stress. After a brief breathing exercise, I guide people through writing prompts which I've written to help them express themselves, externalise the stress, reflect and discover, and explore next steps. Participants record feeling better after the 90-minute session than they did when they arrived.

I'm sharing the session with you in this book so that you can dip into it whenever you need to. Here are some notes on how best to approach these journal questions or any journaling you do.

- Remember there is no right or wrong way to write or feel.
- Leave self-judgement and self-criticism out of this exercise, self-compassion is the vibe we're after.
- Minimise distractions and make sure that you're comfortable (blankets, candles, essential oils, and a tasty hot drink set me up).
- Try not to overthink things but instead trust what pops up for you whilst you're feeling focused, relaxed, and in tune with yourself.
- Trust yourself and those instincts of yours.
- Journaling doesn't necessarily feel fun nor easy so do take breaks if you need to.
- Take some deep breaths to ground and calm yourself.

Finally, I've included how long we'd typically spend on a question, but please feel free to ignore those timings and take the time you need. Here we go!

1. Brain-dump all the things which are causing you stress right now, no matter how big or small. [10 minutes]

_____

_____

_____

_____

_____

_____

_____

_____

_____

_____

2. When it comes to weather, meteorological agencies always give storms and hurricanes a different name. For example, we had Storm Eunice, here in the UK, in 2022. Go through the list you've just written and assign each a hurricane name. My biggest source of stress now is called Hurricane Nadia. [2 minutes]

_____

_____

_____

_____

3. Scan your body from the tips of your toes to the top of your head, whilst thinking of those stressful hurricanes you've just named. Take your time to scan each part of your body, to tune in with it and to fully understand what it feels to be holding that stress. Where is it most prevalent? Where are you holding it? [5 minutes]

_____

_____

_____

_____

_____

_____

_____

_____

_____

4. Remain tuned in to yourself, and brainstorm at least three things (more if you can think of them) that you could do to eliminate or reduce the stress itself or the effects of the stress. [5 minutes]

_____

_____

_____

_____

_____

_____

_____

5. Of those ideas, reflect upon which one is the kindest to you, full of self-compassion, if not necessarily the easiest, and then highlight it in some way [2 minutes]

_____

_____

_____

6. Choose the biggest stress hurricane from your list. Time travel back to a time before the storm. Are the causes, the chain of events, the reasons, the 'why' clear yet? If so, write about it in as much clarity as you've mustered. If not, turn to one of the other stress hurricanes and work through that in the same way. [8 minutes]

_____

_____

_____

_____

_____

_____

_____

_____

7. Think of someone you care about. Imagine they're right in the middle of *your* stress hurricane. Write them a letter including the advice you'd give. [11 minutes]

_____

_____

_____

_____

_____

_____

_____

_____

_____

_____

_____

8. Some of our greatest learnings come from the most horrible and hardest of places. Consider what this stress hurricane has taught you, perhaps, about communication, boundaries, your resilience, your support network. What might you do differently, going forward? [5 minutes]

_____

_____

_____

_____

_____

_____

9. What stressbusters are healthy and kind for you short- and long-term? What brings you joy, lights you up, makes you happy? How have you soothed and grounded yourself in the past when you've been frustrated or angry, or felt trapped, hopeless, or overwhelmed? Write a list of as many as you can think of and, if it helps, write them inside the image of a

box representing your self-care toolkit – because that's what these things are. [6 minutes]

_____

_____

_____

_____

_____

_____

_____

_____

_____

10. Complete this sentence:
   Peace would look and feel like... [2 minutes]

_____

_____

_____

After the session I always ask the participants to:

- schedule in some stress-busting activities, so that when they look at their calendar, they see things to look forward to as they ride out these hurricanes.
- choose one of the actions or solutions they brainstormed or wrote in the letter to someone they cared about, and then do it.

Building resilience

After we move through and past stress, we can do lots of things to increase our resilience, learning from those experiences, so we're prepared should we ever be in that position again.

There's something so satisfyingly calming about feeling prepared for stress, in being tooled-up. Of course, not everything in life is preventable. Yet just knowing that we're equipped to handle and manage a stressor? Well, that brings confidence and steadfastness.

The next section presents suggestions aplenty of ways we can use our hindsight as our *foresight* for what's to come, and thus manage future stress. I do offer a caveat: you don't need to try all the ideas right away. To be here, reading now, means you've already (probably) taken on too much.

Make space for yourself

If you find yourself overextended and overcommitted, it is important to alleviate that pressure as quickly as possible to make way for breathing space. Consider what can be cancelled, delegated, postponed, or re-negotiated, and then be sure to cancel, delegate, postpone and renegotiate it. *Your health is truly the most important thing.*

_____

_____

_____

_____

_____

_____

_____

Track time

If you find yourself complaining about 'not having enough time', then it makes sense to properly understand where your time goes. Whenever I start feeling as though I've lost my grasp on time, I use Clockify, an app which is free and simple to use. I log my time and rather than being constrictive (like in my old accountancy days), I find it oddly empowering. Doing so always, always shows me that I do have enough time; I'm just not particularly fulfilled by how I'm using it.

If you really can't be bothered to do this, consider an app to measure the time you're on your smartphone. Lots of smartphones now come with this built-in (see the device wellbeing settings). It might be that you're fully comfortable with the time spent on the device, or it might be a little sobering. Don't shame yourself though, whatever you do! Smartphones are designed to be boundaryless and to keep us online; it's how they make their money.

I'm always a little shocked by the time I spend on my phone, especially because I'm actively trying *not* to be on my phone. It's always about an hour a day but sometimes that creeps up to three. Knowing I'm on my phone for that amount of time doesn't sit right with me, *especially* when I'm feeling time poor. Yet I do have time. I just need to reclaim it from Mark Zuckerberg!

Thankfully, I use App Blocker, which tells me exactly what I've been up to (emails, our daughter's school app, Google, etc) and allows me to set up profiles to block certain websites (news, Reddit, Twitter) and set limits on others (Instagram and Pinterest).

Buy time

There's an awkward inner dialogue that comes as a knee-jerk reaction when we commit to something we don't want to do. It's felt in the way one's stomach drops or in the immediate sense of dread after agreeing to do this activity.

The next time something is requested, buy time. Instead of the automatic 'yes', try answering with some of these scripts:

I'll get back to you once I've had a chance to check my diary.

Can I get back to you?

When do you need to know?

I need to double-check some details before I can confirm or decline, so please leave it with me.

Later, sense-check how it feels to commit or decline the request. Is it an opportunity that energises you, or does it make you feel all... well... *ugh*? If you say yes, what are you saying no to? Is the activity worth more, honestly, than whatever is being edged out?

In addition, a request to babysit might not just be saying yes to babysitting. It could mean using up fuel and your time. On the other hand, it might mean saying yes to connecting with a young person you love and adore spending time with.

Perhaps you don't enjoy babysitting and in saying yes to this request, will miss spending time in a way you might enjoy, perhaps missing a favourite TV show, a class, or a night out with friends.

Trust yourself. Weigh it up. And then, only then, respond. Give yourself the space to decide whether you really do, or really don't, want to.

Start subtracting

This is one of my very favourite approaches to managing stress: if life doesn't add up, start subtracting. Instead of adding this project and that responsibility on top of what's already a topsy-turvy platform of busyness, stress, and anxiety, start removing the things which aren't important, no longer serve, or keep tripping you up. For example, remove toxic people, working outside of work hours, clutter, bad habits, meaningless tasks, obligations, using social media, social events you don't enjoy, gossip, half-finished and never-to-be-begun-again craft projects, expired ideas, email subscriptions, outdated clothing, outdated food, and so on. Remove as much as possible that's creating unnecessary noise and cluttering up your life and headspace.

Things I could remove:

_____

_____

_____

_____

Look ahead

'Adulting' means we might have dentist appointments, car MOTs, other things in the diary which are non-negotiable; we can't subtract them because they're important or simply necessary. However, it's difficult to feel hope and optimism for the future when we look ahead and see that our schedules are crammed with all the things we *must* do and not a whole lot of things we *want* to do.

Studies show that when we have a holiday booked the anticipation of that holiday brings us joy. So much so, that the day before the holiday is the most joyous of all the days – even more so than the actual holiday itself! Just anticipating something that we view as a positive experience, can make us happy, therefore reducing stress. It doesn't need to be something as big as a holiday; it could be a coffee date with a friend, a trip to the cinema, a day off work all to yourself, planting some bulbs in the garden, going to a concert, or whatever *you'd* look forward to.

Keep a stress log

Keeping a stress log can be cathartic as it gives us the chance to get it all out. Brain-dump it all, every last ounce or cause of stress.

Then, take a break and return to the list with the intention of being solution-focused. The aim is to tackle these sources of stress, one by one. (*whispers*: 'I am not an "eat the frog"-er.') I start with the easiest ones as I find it gives me momentum and helps my problem-solving muscle to warm up.

An example of a stressor might be that due to current financial hardship or hardship in the past, opening the post you receive causes you stress and worry.

An example of some solutions might be to:

* automate paying of bills if you can.
* opt out of receiving postal statements, having them emailed instead.
* ask someone to help you if you have a back-log.
* speak with organisations like the Citizens Advice Bureau if you need financial help and advice.

- apply for benefits or grants you might be eligible for.

My stress log:

_____
_____
_____
_____
_____
_____
_____
_____

My stressor I will tackle first:

_____
_____
_____
_____
_____
_____
_____

Actions I could take:

_____
_____
_____
_____

Visualise your stress bucket

Earlier in the book, we explored the concept of a stress bucket, and I think visualising *your* stress bucket serves as an effective way to see your current capacity and what you might do to increase it if needed.

Draw a bucket below. If you feel you have a big capacity for stress, make it a bigger bucket. Similarly, if you feel you have a small capacity for stress, make it a smaller one. No self-judgement, though – meet yourself where you are.

Draw a tap on the side of the bucket.

Now, write in the bucket all your current stresses and strains. This could be a relationship that's feeling unbalanced, money worries, a heavy workload, an unresolved argument, or perhaps you've been unwell lately. Keep writing until you feel you've got them all inside the bucket.

Next to the tap, write down all the tools, coping skills, and activities you have or do which help you to empty the bucket, relieve or alleviate that stress you're experiencing. Perhaps you don't have a particularly long list next to that tap – that's okay – look through some of the pages on this book for inspiration of things you might adapt and adopt to prevent your bucket from overflowing.

Build your self-esteem

If we perpetually feel unworthy and not-enough, then we might find that we've unintentionally lowered the standards in terms of what we might put up with. If there's this sense that we don't feel as though we are enough, then we might seek to prove our enough-ness by doing as much as we can, saying yes to every demand, request, or hint so that we can evidence our usefulness.

In case nobody has ever told you: you are worthy no matter what you do or don't do. You are worthy of all that's good and all that's golden in life, just as you are enough as you are right in this moment and every moment that preceded or that follows. It's not something that needs to be proven; it just *is*. As we know for certain the sun will rise and set again, you are certainly worthy and enough. Always.

There's a direct correlation between our inner worlds and our outer worlds, with our outer worlds quite often being a reflection on what's going on inside our minds. Our inner worlds influence our behaviours and actions so you might be taking on more than you can cope with, but you might also be putting up with shoddy behaviour from others and holey knickers when you deserve so much more.

Here are some things you could try, appreciating that they sound easy but putting them into consistent practise so often is not:

- Stop trying to please everyone else and be honest with yourself about your needs and wants.

- Random acts of self-kindness. Picking up the groceries? Add a bunch of tulips to the basket. Linger in the bath. Watch that film everyone's talking about. Replace or mend the holey things.

- Take moments to reflect on and celebrate life's highlights and wins, and don't brush them away as luck or unimportant. Allow yourself a pat on the back and to enjoy that sense of accomplishment.

- Be a learner, which means trying new things but also making mistakes. Stop ruminating on all the 'could haves' and 'should haves'.

- Create a comfort zone for yourself, literally. It's a space or place that's comforting and soothing where we can flake out when life has asked lots of us.

• Take care of boundaries, communicating your limits in all relationships, including at work. You're allowed to be clear about what's not okay and what doesn't align.

• Don't get too comfortable. Confidence comes from doing the things we didn't think we could do, so make sure there's some stepping out of that comfort zone too.

• Be the very best friend to yourself that you could ever have asked for. Choose to contradict any negative self-talk, encourage yourself, big yourself up when needed, smile at yourself in the mirror, and be patient and loving.

Get clear on your values

Values are beliefs that underpin our standards and principles of behaviour. They embody our priorities in life, what really matters to us, and they motivate and guide our way. Your own values will be different to those of another, and that difference plays into individuality and autonomy in your own life. They help you proceed with intention, provide a secure sense of identity, of who you truly are, and steer you away from anything that's not in keeping with them.

Knowing our values is super important because they help us to orient our decisions and actions so that we're living authentically and purposefully.

There are so many 'values-finding' exercises on the internet; just pop 'what are my core values?' or 'personal values quiz' into a search engine. But, as we're here and the aim of this book is to meet you where you are, here's a list copied (with permission) from The Berkeley Wellbeing Institute.

Consider which of these values resonate with you and circle them. Highlight your top three to five values, those you feel strongest about, and then in the coming weeks use these to help you make more value-driven decisions.

It's worth noting that working within a sector, industry, or organisation where the professional values are at conflict with our own personal values can be one heck of a stressor.

- acceptance
- accomplishment
- accountability
- accuracy
- achievement
- adaptability
- adventurousness
- agreeableness
- alertness
- altruism
- ambition
- amiability
- amusement
- amusingness
- appreciation
- art
- articulateness
- assertiveness
- athleticism
- attentiveness
- authenticity
- awe
- balance
- beauty
- being admirable
- being dynamic
- being earnest
- being famous
- being folksy
- being frank
- being methodical
- being personable
- being reasonable
- being skilled
- being thoughtful
- being understanding
- benevolence
- bliss
- boldness
- bravery

- brilliance
- calmness
- candour
- capability
- carefulness
- caring
- cautiousness
- certainty
- challenge
- charisma
- charity
- charm
- cheerfulness
- citizenship
- clarity
- cleanliness
- clear-headedness
- cleverness
- comfort
- commitment
- common sense
- communication
- community
- compassion
- competence
- complexity
- confidence
- connection
- conscientiousness
- conservativeness
- consideration
- consistency
- constructiveness
- contemplation
- contentment
- contribution
- control
- conviction
- cooperation
- courage
- courteousness
- craftiness
- creativity
- credibility
- curiosity
- daringness
- decency
- decisiveness
- dedication
- deep thought
- democracy
- dependability

- determination
- devotion
- dignity
- diligence
- discipline
- discovery
- diversity
- drive
- dualism
- dutifulness
- easygoingness
- education
- effectiveness
- efficiency
- elegance
- eloquence
- emotional awareness
- emotional control
- empathy
- empowerment
- endurance
- energy
- enjoyment
- enthusiasm
- equality
- ethics
- excellence
- excitement
- expedience
- experimenting
- exploration
- expressiveness
- extraordinary experiences
- fairness
- faith
- faithfulness
- family
- farsightedness
- fashion
- feelings
- fidelity
- flair
- flexibility
- focus
- foresight
- forgiving
- forthrightness
- fortitude
- freedom
- freethinking
- friendliness
- friendship

- fun
- fun-loving attitude
- generosity
- gentleness
- genuineness
- giving
- glamorousness
- good-naturedness
- goodness
- grace
- graciousness
- gratitude
- greatness
- growth
- happiness
- hard work
- harmony
- health
- helpfulness
- heroicness
- honesty
- honour
- hope
- humbleness
- humility
- humour
- idealism
- imagination
- incisiveness
- independence
- individualism
- individuality
- influence
- innovation
- insightfulness
- inspiration
- integrity
- intelligence
- intensity
- intuitiveness
- inventiveness
- joy
- justice
- kindness
- knowledge
- lawfulness
- leadership
- learning
- liberty
- life direction
- life experience
- likability

- logic
- love
- loyalty
- mastery
- maturity
- mellowness
- moderation
- modesty
- motivation
- neatness
- neutrality
- newness
- niceness
- objectivity
- open-mindedness
- openness
- optimism
- order
- organization
- originality
- passion
- patience
- patriotism
- peace
- peacefulness
- performance
- perseverance
- persistence
- playfulness
- pleasure
- poise
- positive attitude
- positivity
- potential
- power
- practicality
- preciseness
- principles
- productivity
- professionalism
- prosperity
- protection
- punctuality
- purpose
- quality
- rationality
- realism
- recognition
- recreation
- reflection
- relaxation
- reliability

- resourcefulness
- respect
- respect for others
- responsibility
- restraint
- results-oriented
- rigor
- risk
- romance
- satisfaction
- security
- self-awareness
- self-improvement
- self-reliance
- self-respect
- self-sufficiency
- selflessness
- sensitivity
- serenity
- service
- simplicity
- smarts
- sociability
- social connection
- sophistication
- speed
- spirituality
- spontaneity
- stability
- status
- steadiness
- strength
- structure
- studiousness
- success
- sweetness
- sympathy
- teamwork
- tenderness
- thinking big
- thoroughness
- tidiness
- timeliness
- tolerance
- tradition
- tranquillity
- transformation
- trust
- truth
- unity
- variety
- vivaciousness

- warmth
- wealth
- well-roundedness
- wisdom
- wit

Smartphones for good

According to the Uswitch service, in 2021, 88 per cent of the population of the UK owned a smartphone. These devices of ours have quite a bad reputation because of the way they're built to be addictive. But with some nifty changing of settings and installing of apps, we can turn them into a tool that's helpful.

Turn off notifications

When we think of sound as being a distinct call to action, there's nothing quite like the pinging and ringing of a phone to grab our attention and distract us from all else. They're designed to interrupt whatever we're doing so we'll pick up our phone – literally when it tells us to. Not only is this a cause of noise pollution if all our phones are at it, but it's also a known trigger of stress and anxiety. Turning off the notifications prevents all of that and also means we regain control of when and how we check in and, often, it's that sense of control that's amiss when we're feeling stressed.

Blue light filter

The blue light that our phones emit has been shown to disrupt the quality of our sleep by suppressing the release of melatonin which is a hormone that makes us feel sleepy. Sleep is a crucial component in our resilience against stress.

Rather than suppress the hormones we need, let's instead suppress the thing that causes the damage: the blue light. Most smartphones these days come with a built-in eye comfort shield or similar setting. If not, you can install apps like:

- f.lux
- Night Shift
- Twilight
- Blue Light Filter
- EasyEyes

Apps

Having a set of helpful apps already installed on your phone can be super useful for the times we might be in the thick of it and nothing else seems to be working for us.

A gazillion apps are available, and more are being released all the time, so I'm going to mention just a few that I've either installed or heard really great things about:

- **Calm:** I pay for a subscription to Calm but there are guided meditations, stories and soundscapes which are also available in the free version. There's a whole section for children which our daughter Peggy and I love. (Sometimes those are comforting for me too!) **Headspace** is another app, like **Calm,** that I've heard great things about, as is **UCLA Mindful** which is completely free.

• **Spotify**: This is another one I pay for but it's the most used app on my phone. I've created and I enjoy my playlists, and I also love other people's playlists. If I'm in need of calm, I search for 'calming playlists' or 'binaural beats'. It's great to just pop those on in a hurry and get listening. **Aumio** is said to have a great selection of soundscapes too.

• **Wordly**: This is basically a copy of the well-known word game Wordle, but I love that, as well as the daily puzzle (which is different from Wordle's daily puzzle), I can do more than just the one puzzle per day. When I'm sitting waiting for a meeting or appointment and I can feel my stress levels rising, I dive into this app and do some puzzles, and it keeps me calm. **Colorfy** is another app I've heard people have used to soothe themselves, and **Stress Relief Coloring**.

• **AppBlock:** I love that this app (the free version) keeps my phone usage in check and allows me to block apps and websites like the news apps and websites I've been known to doom-scroll through.

- **Breathly**: This free app guides the user through a breathing exercise. It's also possible to change the breathing exercise itself in the settings. I like it because if I'm in a public place and want to take control of my breath, then I can focus on the screen as I do so. Others I've heard good things about are **Breathe2Relax, BreathWrk,** and **Dandelion (Breathing Games)**.

- **Moodflow**: I've heard such good things about this mood journal and symptom tracker. I wish I'd known about it when I was in the middle of the stressful periods of my life. If I had tracked causal situations and events, it might have helped me to make sense of some of things.

Start a new hobby

A hobby is something that we regularly do in our non-work time simply because it's fun and enjoyable. It's not something we *have* to do, rather we *choose* to do it. Hobbies are beneficial to our mental health, they can take our minds off things, act as an outlet for creativity, increase mindfulness, and provide a break from the hustle and bustle of life. Sometimes they also bring on a sense of eustress, that good stress stuff that's exhilarating, exciting and fun.

You might already have a hobby that's fallen by the wayside in recent times because of everything else you're having to get a handle on. Try picking it back up, even if it's just for 15 minutes a day, to experience the benefits. Don't have a hobby? Think of an activity that's piqued your interest in the past, choose something from the list below, or search the internet for ideas. If a hobby is not for you, don't fret; just move onto trying something else until you find the thing that brings enjoyment to life.

- Play a musical instrument, listen to music, make music, dance, sing, or rap.

- Draw, paint, colour in, scrapbook, or do origami.
- Knit, crochet, sew, quilt, cross-stitch, make jewellery or candles.
- Journal, write stories or poetry, practise calligraphy, read, blog, or vlog.
- Complete jigsaw puzzles, play video games or board games, or work on puzzle books.
- Take up gardening, upcycling, restoration, DIY, antiquing, or woodwork.
- Do any form of exercise.
- Bake, take a cookery class, make pottery, or try pickling.
- Volunteer.
- Birdwatch, bee-keep, or butterfly-watch.
- Learn about astronomy, go geocaching, hiking, camping, or sailing.
- Start a collection of rocks, stamps, or comics.
- Learn a new skill: juggle, use a hula-hoop or pogo stick, practise another language, do magic tricks, or try photography.

Get moving

There's far too much evidence to show that exercise plays a vital role in helping us to manage stress for me *not* to mention it here, but I think we can agree that when stressed to the hilt, exercise just feels like another thing to consider and add in when mental and physical energy levels are already depleted. Nevertheless, exercise can boost self-confidence and energy, enhance moods by stimulating the production of endorphins, improve sleep quality and cognitive function as well as lower stress hormones. It's basically a powerhouse.

It's finding exercise that we *enjoy* that's pivotal.

Exercise is basically any activity that requires exerting some sort of physical effort and movement, an activity which will increase heart rate. We do not have to train for a marathon, take that aerobics class, or commit to some other form of exercise that fills us with dread before we even get going. We really, *really* don't. Things which are *also* exercise: jumping on a kid's trampoline, dancing around the living room, skipping with a skipping rope, wave-jumping, sex, flying a kite, cartwheeling, hopscotch, going for a walk, and a natter with a friend.

Stop the ANTs

Our thoughts can become habitual as much as our behaviours can and when we're feeling all out of sorts, our internal dialogue can become all out of sorts too. When the immediate response to something is a torrential stream, though, these are called Automatic Negative Thoughts (ANTs). ANTs are often how those awful downward mental spirals begin, with us automatically berating ourselves over every mishap, misadventure, thing we feel we've said that was wrong, thing we feel we did wrong, or times when we've been wrong.

The trouble is, when we constantly call ourselves names, those names start to get absorbed into the fabric of our being and they change the way we see ourselves – for the worse.

If you tell someone something enough, they'll believe you.

Things won't always pan out as we'd hoped and when things do go lopsided, that's truly part and parcel of life – for everyone, despite how things might seem for us looking in on someone else's life. We're not fools, silly, stupid, hopeless, helpless, awful, rubbish, idiots [insert not-so-nice name you might call yourself here], slipping up 'now and then', or even 'more often than not'. There is no instruction manual for an individual life anyway; it is all a learning curve.

Let's look at some ways we might try to stop the ANTs:

• Replace the 'should' statements with 'could'. Instead of lamenting that you 'should' be able to do this or that, swap it with 'could'. This simple switch makes you feel as though you have choices – which you always do. You might feel as though you 'should' exercise every day but that's a pressure or expectation that's coming from outside of you. When you change it to 'could' you begin to feel and see you have options which come from inside of you.

• Recognise it for what it is and name it. Try to catch yourself as the negative thoughts start and say to yourself, 'Oh, these are those ANTs'. At that moment, try to do something to jolt you out of your mental state; watch funny cats on YouTube, call that humorous friend, or listen to that song you know all the lyrics to and sing it oh-so-loudly.

• Collect compliments. When someone says something lovely – whether that's face-to-face, in an email, on social media, wherever – make a note of it. Screen grab it and save these comments somewhere that's easily accessible. Then when the ANTs start up, show them the evidence to the contrary.

• Live in the grey. Life isn't black or white. It's not so extreme, and there are millions of shades of grey between those two opposites. And that's where we reside. There's so much more nuance to life than right or wrong and good or bad and perfection or failure. Those ANTs? They come from a place of black and white thinking, and we can counterattack by pausing for a moment and moving from the drastic to a space that's more elastic. For example, maybe the job interview didn't go so well, and that sucks, but it doesn't mean we're a useless failure. It could mean that the job wasn't right for us. Or, that we did well to answer and stay calm when presented with some particularly challenging questions.

Consider adaptogens

Plants and mushrooms which help decrease fatigue, exhaustion, and the effects of stress; and increase our tolerance to stress and balance our hormones, are known as adaptogens. In essence, they work to restore balance to the body. They generally come in capsule form or as powders to add to food and drink. Teas and tinctures available too. Supplementing with adaptogens won't help you to out-run stress – ultimately, there are underlying issues which need addressing. They do, however, support recovery and regulation of the stress response.

Research shows that adaptogens can promote restful sleep, boost energy, and return our body to homeostasis, thereby re-establishing the balance of our body's physiological processes. Rhodiola is one of the most studied adaptogens and the results of those studies show the efficacy of rhodiola in recovery from burnout and increasing energy and stamina levels alongside increasing resistance to stress and decreasing fatigue and symptoms of anxiety. More than 200 studies have been conducted on ashwagandha (I mix this with turmeric) which show that it can strengthen the immune system, is a natural stress reliever, promotes relaxation, helps relieve adrenal fatigue, and improves memory. Other adaptogens which have been shown to help relieve stress include ginseng, holy basil, astragalus, cordyceps, schisandra chinensis, and jiaogulan, to name a few.

It is wise to speak with your doctor before taking any adaptogens, because some existing medical conditions and/or medications mightn't be a good match.

Try meditating

Meditation is a practice which brings your attention and focus to the present moment without judgement or criticism. The aim is to notice and observe thoughts as they come and go but not to engage with them. It's very much about *being* rather than doing. Often there's an anchor to focus on whether that be breathing or a sound.

When we think of meditating, we picture someone sitting cross-legged on a mat, with their eyes closed and the ability to clear their mind with ease. Meditation *can* absolutely be that, but it can also be something we do when lying down, in the bath, on a walk, in a queue, washing the dishes, cleaning, listening to calming music, gardening, and so on. You can get into a meditative state anywhere and for any length of time.

We think that if our minds wander then we've failed at meditation; yet noticing that our minds have wandered and bringing the focus back to the moment is akin to practising dribbling the ball and aiming shots in a basketball ring to progress.

When we're stressed, our minds are often racing and

feeling out of control. Meditation can feel difficult, and we can easily slip into a sense of having failed. That's why guided meditations are so useful because they guide you and bring you back to the breath, the onus isn't on you. In a sense, you can lean on someone else for support via the guided meditation. Reasons to give meditation a go as a stress management tool are plentiful: it lowers stress, anxiety, and blood pressure; increases a sense of calm, focus, concentration, and peace; enhances empathy, compassion, kindness, creativity, and your immune system; develops mental and self-awareness; improves mood; and helps clear the mind to give it a break from all else.

Fix your sleep

Good quality sleep is imperative in helping to build our resilience to stress, but it's one of those chicken and egg situations, because whilst sleep *does* help us manage stress, stress also directly and tremendously impacts our sleep. Trying to fix sleep without trying to manage the stress is futile, like pouring tea from a chocolate teapot.

Once you start managing your stress, sleep could very likely improve too. Here are some things you can do to help nudge it in the right direction.

- Create a bedtime routine which focuses on winding down and relaxation. Repeat the same routine at the same time every night so that your body gets used to the cues that the day is ending and it's time to rest.

- Try to maintain a sleep schedule, going to bed and getting up at the same time, even on weekends.

- Try not to use your devices an hour before bed and

keep them out of the bedroom. We might, for example, associate a laptop with work, and it can be difficult to switch off with that beacon in the bedroom, glaring and blaring, 'Work!'

• Limit caffeine, sugar, and alcohol intake.

• Keep a notebook by the bed to brain dump all those pesky thoughts that pipe up just as you're trying to pipe down for the night.

• Shorten naps during the day and making sure not to nap after 3pm.

• Blackout blinds can help, as can having a window open (if it's safe).

• Soak in an Epsom salt bath or foot spa.

• Use calming essential oils in the shower or a calming pillow spray.

Pack your bag

When our daughter was much younger, I started carrying a few items in my rucksack to help soothe her when she seemed overstimulated on our way home from a party or soft play, for example. I'd have a fleece blanket, some slipper socks, wireless headphones to use with the Calm app on my phone, snacks, lip balm, fidget toys, and a rollerball of lavender oil. It worked a treat, and still does. In fact, nowadays, I'm just as likely to dive in and use these tools to anchor and comfort myself too.

Likewise, wherever you go, take a bag of tricks to help calm and comfort you.

Check-in

It's much easier to course-correct when we realise that we're going off-piste sooner rather than later, whether professionally or personally. Choosing to narrow the window for our reflections means we're more likely to remember the whereabouts and 'how abouts' – this is, the details – accurately.

Consider winding down your days or weeks or months with a debrief, giving yourself the chance to consider when and how you felt with an investigative head-on. Doing this holistically, including the whole self and all the bits and bobs of life in one reflection, will not only help you to understand your values but also to question why some things keep rearing up (or others that didn't turn out as you'd expected) and to identify stressors as they start. Why wait until they've become bigger down the line? Noticing recurring themes is like panning for gold dust.

No matter how big or how small, what went well today, this week, or this month?

_____

_____

_____

_____

_____

_____

What didn't go well and why?

_____

_____

_____

_____

_____

_____

The things I'm stuck on, or the recurring issues or stressors, are:

_____

_____

_____

_____

_____

_____

What I need to do about those:

_____
_____
_____
_____
_____
_____

Lesson log, or 'what I've learned':

_____
_____
_____
_____
_____

My next priorities:

_____
_____
_____
_____
_____

Write a care guide

When you buy a houseplant, it comes with a care guide: 'This plant likes direct sunlight', 'It needs to be fed once a month', 'Only water when the top two inches of the soil seem dry', etc., etc. Those instructions are pertinent to that plant and that plant only. Place another plant in direct sunlight and it might wither away.

Being a plant parent means you also become accustomed to a certain plant's ways. The subtle wilting that says, 'I need a drink,' and the yellowing of leaves that says, 'Er, ahem – I wasn't *that* thirsty.' Each plant behaves in different ways under differing conditions.

We're all like houseplants, in that we, too, all behave differently under differing conditions. Unfortunately, we don't come with a care guide when we're born, but it's never too late to write one, including notes about conditions and circumstances under which we thrive or wilt. Keep updating it as and when you notice something new. If we feel comfortable doing so, we can share the care guide, or snippets, with those we trust and might be able to help us in specific situations.

Some examples:

- When I spend too much time being sociable, I need space to myself to recover, preferably with a blanket, some calming essential oils, and no electronic devices.

- If I drink caffeine, it makes me anxious, so I need to take decaf tea or coffee when visiting other people's houses.

- XYZ are people I trust, and they listen well when I'm spiralling or need to talk, so I'll reach out to them.

- I work best between the hours of 8am and noon so that's when I do my hardest tasks.

- Talking on the telephone or in a Zoom meeting is quite stressful, because I worry I mightn't remember what's been agreed upon or discussed. So I'll always ask if something can be discussed via email or text. Or an email to follow-up can be sent to make sure I've recalled the important points, understood context correctly, and am aware of any further deliverables.

- I get hot in bed at night and sleep best with a window open.

• I forget to make drinks when I'm focused, so I prepare enough to see me through until lunchtime or home time, and then put them in plain sight in my workspace.

My care guide:

_____

_____

_____

_____

_____

_____

_____

_____

_____

_____

_____

_____

_____

_____

A note on support systems

One of the most wonderful ways to manage stress is having a group of trusted people to lean on and rely on, who are there through thick and thin, happy to deliver practical help and support, or just to hold your hand and listen. These people are your backup, a cavalry to call, a support system, and I highly recommend leaning on them when everything gets too much or seems to be heading that way, as a first port of call.

If it's so great, then why is the support network way, *way* down on the list of stress management tools and tips? I want to acknowledge that so many people do not feel they have such a ready-made accessible support system. For many reasons, loneliness is prevalent and it's sadly all too common for people to feel alone or as though they're a burden, with nowhere to turn or nobody to call for much-needed and much-deserved help and support.

If that's the case for you, I want to reassure you that support systems aren't always made up of people we've known for aeons or lifetimes. They're not always our peer groups either. And that's okay. It might not feel like it but there is help and support available which you *are* worthy and deserving of no matter what. Support systems *can* be built.

There's a website aptly named The Hub of Hope at www.hubofhope.co.uk, and it's incredible! You type in your postcode and what you need help with (stress, loneliness, anxiety, whatever it is) and the hub will provide a list of organisations and peer support groups which were set up by people who care and want to help. They're there for you, and they'll know of additional support too. If you're feeling too nervous to call, you can usually email.

Healing

When we've been through a drawn-out period of stress, we're changed by that emotionally, mentally, and physically, and, usually, we are thrown by it. We can feel as though we've lost our way and far from who we were, are, or who we want to be. Feeling lost can be a stressor itself, and having a life full of stressors can cause us to feel lost. It's a catch-22.

We rewild nature to return it to its uncultivated state, and in the next section of the book we're going to look at how we rewild ourselves; reclaim our resources; our time, energy, headspace, sense of peace, heal and find our way back home to ourselves. It's not a quick nor easy process, this healing stage, and it takes time, love, and patience.

Seven types of rest

The impact of stress isn't one to be underestimated and, as such, healing can take longer than we might anticipate or hope for. Armed now with some robust and paramount stress management tools, it's time to recover, relax and *rest*.

Rest doesn't just occur when we're asleep. In fact, if we spend our days zipping and zooming from one task to another, multi-tasking and switching between tasks willy-nilly, then when we lay down at night, our brain will probably start swimming through all that happened, might happen, or will happen. Sleep might feel elusive. This is because we haven't had enough rest during the day or not enough of the right type of rest.

Similarly, it explains why we might wake up feeling exhausted and not at all prepared, energetically, for the day ahead. According to physician Saundra Dalton-Smith, M.D., to feel tip-top, there are seven different types of rest to incorporate into our days and ways.

Mental rest

Where you give your brain a break from having to process, think, and do. Our brains aren't ever truly resting: while we're giving them space, they're assimilating, storing, filtering, learning, and making connections. When we don't give our brains a rest in this way, it affects our working memory, our concentration, and the ability to connect the dots and sleep.

Mental rest looks like taking regular breaks from work, every 90 minutes or so, writing down thoughts and tasks, exercise, meditation, breathing exercises, and stepping away from screens.

Physical rest

When we think of resting, it's usually physical resting, and we most likely acknowledge and make time for. Physical rest can be passive, like when we're asleep and napping, or it can be active, like when we're doing yoga or having a massage. It's when we allow the tension from our body to dissipate and give it relief from the aches and pains.

Sensory rest

We take in a constant stream of stimuli through our senses. Without taking a break from it, those stimuli can become overwhelming and overstimulating, eventually causing a sensory overload if it becomes too much to process.

Sensory rest might be popping on some noise-cancelling

headphones, going off to a quiet spot, turning off bright lights, taking a break from screens, listening to some calming music, removing any uncomfortable clothes, or soothing your senses with essential oils or a fluffy blanket.

Creative rest

We also need rest from all that coordinating, problem-solving, brainstorming, and creating that we do, particularly if we work in roles which regularly require it.

Creative rest happens when we tap into feeling inspired, experience awe, and rekindle our imaginations with the arts. This might look like watching a sunset, going to a museum or art gallery, looking at photographs, or going to a concert or listening to music, for example. When a solution or idea comes to you when sunbathing on a beach or while taking a shower, that's a sign that you're creatively rested.

Emotional rest

Ever felt taken for granted, undervalued, and unappreciated? Perhaps you felt your well of empathy run dry, being unable to connect with someone else in that way when you're usually so adept at it. Those were or are the times we're in need of emotional rest. We're emotion-ed out, likely because we've given so much of ourselves to others when they've needed support.

Emotional rest looks and feels like time and space to speak

openly and freely. It's also time spent with people with whom we can hang out, laugh, and be ourselves. It is also time alone, away from responsibilities.

Social rest

Relationships ebb and flow, and some drain and others revive us. Too much time spent being drained will deplete and tire us, and we'll need social rest from those. Spend time with those who are inspiring, uplifting, grounding, and enjoyable to be around for a dose of social rest. Of course, sometimes, especially if we're introverted, we just need a break from *all* things social.

Spiritual rest

Our spirituality is what gives our everyday lives meaning in a way that's bigger than who we are. It includes those all-encompassing and oftentimes inexplicable experiences of love, peace, belonging, acceptance, gratitude, and awe. It's the interconnectedness we find, and experience, to moments, nature, faith, and other people, and is often described as sacred, divine, cosmic.

Spiritual rest might be meditation, or it might be prayer. It can often be found in exploring nature, being part of a community initiative, or understanding your purpose and applying it.

Create a bliss list

When we're up to our eyeballs in stress, positive things can rankle because they're so far from where we are. So, there might be some resistance to this next suggestion but do sit with it and take notice of how you and your body react to certain situations and people. It's the 'bliss' we're after in this exercise: the things or people that were uplifting, eased discomfort, lit us up like a lighthouse, gave pep in your step and made you feel warm and bright.

My bliss list:

_____

_____

_____

_____

_____

_____

_____

Create a diss list

It's just as important to understand and be aware of the activities, people and surroundings which leave us feeling less-than, which take and drain and cause frustration. These things will form your diss list, and while it's not the most comfortable of exercises, it's often an enlightening one.

My diss list:

_____

_____

_____

_____

_____

_____

_____

Question whether we're headed in the right direction

When we're lost on a car journey, we recalibrate by telling someone, using Google, or mapping where we want to go. In life, it's also important to know where we're travelling towards, and to question if we're heading in the right direction.

We generally have an idea of what that might look like. Perhaps it's apparent on our Pinterest boards, the 'saved' Instagram posts, the niggling dream that won't go away, a recurring theme in daydreams, or where the mind goes when we're alone.

There are so many reasons we mightn't be heading in that direction, too: fear of making mistakes, fear of being a disappointment, fear of rejection, fear of failure, 'shoulds' and 'should nots', habits, our relationships, a lack of resources, or low self-esteem.

Keep an open mind and consider if where you want to go is different from where you are, especially if you're feeling lost, stifled, or trapped.

Leave all the thoughts that you can't do this or can't do

that behind, just for this exercise. Allow yourself to dream and feel, and to align with what it is you really want.

Here are some writing prompts to help.

1. What would my ideal day look like?

_____

_____

_____

_____

_____

_____

2. Am I happy with my job? If not, why not?

_____

_____

_____

_____

_____

_____

3. What job would I love to do? What career feels more aligned?

_____

_____

_____

_____

4. Something I'd like to do more of, regularly, is...

_____

_____

_____

_____

_____

_____

5. What does 'success' mean to me? What does it look and feel like?

_____

_____

_____

_____

_____

_____

6. What's one habit I'd like to kick to the curb?

_____

_____

_____

_____

_____

7. What's a habit I'd like to start?

8. What's one small step I can take today towards any of this?

9. What or who is holding me back?

10. In a year's time, I'd like to be...

_____

_____

_____

_____

_____

_____

11. If I could change just one thing right now, it'd be...

_____

_____

_____

_____

_____

_____

12. What help do I need right now?

_____

_____

_____

_____

_____

_____

Make sense of something

When we're overwhelmed, everything feels out of sorts. Our external surroundings can follow suit, often becoming a physical representation of what's going on internally. We quickly feel like we're falling out of control in all areas, which is why it makes sense to try and make sense of *something*.

Picking just one thing, however small, and making sense of it, can help us to feel a little better. Usually, it motivates us to do more as we get that dopamine hit which comes when we've achieved something, bringing with it a sense of 'can-do'.

Here are a few starting ideas.

- Make your bed.
- Change your bedding.
- Put the floordrobe in the wash.
- Tackle *that* kitchen drawer, the dumping ground, or the stuck one that causes stress every time you try to open it.
- Weed a patch of the garden.

- Go through your pens and test them, then throw away those which are broken.
- Open and sort your post.
- Replace the broken bulb.
- Clear a kitchen workspace.
- Go through your camera reel and delete any photos you don't want.

Let go of mistakes

If there are regrets, things you feel ashamed of, mistakes, anything that's sitting heavy and making you feel cruddy, write it all out until you have exhausted that list.

Then, safely destroy the list. Shred it, throw it into a fire, tear into a gazillion pieces – obliterate it. But watch them burn, shred, or be obliterated, and as you do so, give your conscious mind a little shake, an 'I'm-moving-on-from-this-now' moment.

It's such a simple exercise but it packs a punch and a half with its symbolism. You're taking those things which are living rent-free in your head, letting them go, and *choosing* to move on anyway.

It sounds all woo-woo, I know, but give it a go. Somehow, it helps draw a line in the sand.

Get clear on who you are not

Feeling rudderless in our own lives really is the pits. Those grotty times, though, are full of valuable, exquisite pearls of wisdom. If being lost teaches us anything, it shows us what *isn't* working, what isn't the right fit, what feels icky, what we don't want to put up with any longer, and what we're *not* – in other words, the circumstances and environments we're *not* thriving in.

Shifting our focus to who we are *not* tells us who we *are*, but for some reason it feels easier to grasp.

For example:

- I am not someone who understands subtext very well.
  > *I am someone who appreciates clear, straight-shooting, honest communication.*

- I am not someone who works well being micromanaged.
  > *I work well under my own steam; I am self-motivated and trustworthy.*

- I am not someone who enjoys mundane tasks.
  > *I enjoy being creative and tasks that challenge me.*

- I am not great at working within a rigid routine.
  > *I value flexibility, freedom, and autonomy over my time.*

- I am not a gossip.
  > *I prefer to be trustworthy.*

Over to you: what are your 'I am nots'?

_____

_____

_____

_____

_____

_____

Lock it in

Despite it being an asset in becoming more resilient to stress, self-care often gets pushed to the wayside when we're stressed. The thing about self-care is that it's the opposite of self-neglect. We can choose to take care of ourselves and then feed all the demands and responsibilities of life with the excess, or we can choose to neglect ourselves, which is akin to running a car on empty: it doesn't get you very far and is damaging to *all* the car's systems.

Because it's so easily shelved, self-care needs locking in. It needs prioritising, scheduling and a mindset switch to change it from a 'nice to do' to a complete non-negotiable part of life. This first non-negotiable is often pivotal. Habit theory proposes that once you've got a habit locked in, it's much easier to pair another habit with it, creating a batch or group of habits together in a routine, than to add each individually.

Look at your bliss list. Consider what tops you up energetically, what steadies and calms you, or what a future you would thank 'now you' for.

Choose just one thing for now as your first non-negotiable so you can get that locked in:

_____

_____

Schedule it in, *right now*, so that this will become a consistent and regular part of each day.

Reset your algorithm

What we consume frequently affects us in more ways than we can probably imagine. If we're taking in inspiring, motivating, and uplifting stuff then we'll likely feel that way. If we surround ourselves with all that's fear-provoking, frightening, and belittling, then that's how we'll start to feel even when we're not consuming anything at all.

It's helpful to think of social media feeds as magazines: what content would we like enough to buy? You wouldn't purchase a sailing magazine if that's not your jam. Likewise, if we follow social media accounts which make us feel less-than-good, then we can do a few things to change what we see when we log on. We can influence the algorithm, so that it shows us more of what we love.

We can unfollow, mute, unfriend, and block. We can also reset our own algorithm by deleting our search history, clearing the caches of web browsers, and following new accounts, ones which are more aligned with the topics and vibes we'd like and linger on. We can tell apps like Instagram what posts we're not interested in by clicking on the three vertical dots on any reels and posts which appear on the 'explore' page, and then tapping on 'this topic doesn't interest me'. Then we can actively like, share and save posts we *are* interested in.

Gradually, we'll notice a shift in what's presented at login. Audit how the content feels and keep repeating the above steps until it feels more *you*.

Be the tryer of new things

Kids are notoriously curious about anything and everything. When we were younger, we, too, were so acquainted with being learners that we fell and got back up again over and over, without inhibition. Everything was new to us; we weren't at all afraid of looking silly or of asking a gazillion questions and not knowing the answers.

Somewhere along the line, we stopped permitting ourselves to be so openly curious and experimental. We, instead, preferred to *look* as though we had our shizz together.

As ever-evolving folk, happiness lies in making those experimental phases life-long.

As we change, it makes sense that what once worked no longer does. Typically, when we feel lost, it's because we've wandered down the wrong path for us. That thought is less daunting, because it means we just need to find the right path, and that comes with walking down a few others until we find the one that feels right.

There are many ways we can step outside of our comfort zones and deviate from what we'd generally do. We might watch a film from a different genre than usual, borrow books from the library that we wouldn't ordinarily read, try new foods and drinks, pair our clothes with different items, paint the walls something other than grey, or beige, or 'greige', register for a class to learn a new skill, etc.

Life really is just a loop of learning. Allow yourself to be a novice.

Pay attention to envy

When envy pipes up, it's such a horrible feeling. It immediately makes the grass look greener elsewhere and tarnishes our perception of our lives as they are. Instead of giving yourself a hard time over an attack of the green-eyed monster, pay close attention to the specific details. They're often a useful guide towards what we'd like to do, be, and have. Ask:

What am I specifically feeling envious of?

_____

_____

_____

_____

What is that envy telling me about what I'd like to do, be, and have?

_____

_____

_____

_____

Reclaiming yourself

When we're feeling lost, our sense of identity can feel all wishy-washy and lost at sea. All is not lost, I promise. Your you-ness is discoverable again. Here's a nifty and fun way to help you unearth it.

Set up a secret Pinterest board and call it something like 'Coming Home'. Use the search bar for topics such as 'summer outfits', 'interior design', or 'colour palettes'. Anything you fancy. Pin everything that piques your interest, takes your fancy, makes you pay attention. Keep mining for images until you have considerably built up the board. Then, when you look at the board in its entirety, notice what colours you're drawn to, what outfits you have really liked, what hobbies seem to have caught your eye, or the recipes that made your mouth water.

You can also do this on Instagram by setting up a folder and saving posts there. Or buying magazines and, using those images, creating some collages.

Only save the things which you feel drawn to: that's the key. It doesn't matter if you don't yet understand the reason that you've saved certain things, because as the library of images builds, patterns will emerge. You might then try to replicate an outfit, recreate one of the recipes, or start researching that stunning holiday destination or career.

Dream a little dream

Fear sometimes squashes our dreams to the point where we cast them aside. But dreams don't let us forget about them; they stay near to the surface, occasionally delivering pangs of recognition.

Those incessant won't-leave-me-alone dreams are the ones I think we're really supposed to be doing and I believe it's our subconscious, our intuition, or something we don't understand telling us and reminding us for a reason.

Dreams are lofty which is the beauty and the blasted about them. They can seem so out of touch, so out of range, so not-for-us, but, at the same time, many people have done what you want to do, proving it's possible, and even sharing the mechanics of how they've done so on YouTube, Google, in books, and in documentaries.

We live in a day and age where plenty of free resources are available. Our dreams don't have to remain pie in the sky, as we can quite literally follow the paths of others to get where they are.

To see what I mean, search online for 'how to [insert dream

here]'. For example, 'how to set up an Etsy store', 'how to train to be an interior designer', 'how to write a book', 'how to find a literary agent', 'how to write a book proposal', 'how to start a blog', and so on. Commit to spending ten minutes each day on a small step towards your dream. Those ten minutes will compound, and you'll hit the tipping point between working towards your dream and living it.

My won't-leave-me-alone dream is:

_____

_____

The first step I can take towards it is:

_____

_____

Consider the younger self

As youngsters, we'd rambunctiously and intuitively seek out joy, prioritising it over all else. To play, to have fun, and to laugh were key drivers in what we'd choose to do.

Sometimes – not always but sometimes – answers can be found in those early years to some of the issues we now face. Which seems odd, right? We assume that as we grow older, we become more knowledgeable, more comfortable in our skins, more 'us'. Sadly, the opposite can too often be true.

Here are a few journal prompts to help dive back in time:

When I was younger, I would while away the time by:

_____

_____

_____

_____

The things which would make me laugh were:

_____

_____

My favourite pastime was:

_____

_____

_____

_____

My most treasured items were:

_____

_____

_____

_____

The songs which bring back memories are:

_____

_____

_____

_____

Now, using the above journal entries as a guide, try those activities again today. You might find you now hate whatever it is, or it might still hold magic. And that? That, too, is *magic*.

Be your own compass

I firmly believe that the answers we seek are usually already within us. This exercise taps into that well of wisdom.

You can choose to travel 10 years ahead, to when you're 10 years older, or 20 years ahead, or 50 years ahead. (Or all three if you're really going for it.) Next, write a letter with advice, guidance, and kind words from the older, future you to the earlier, newer you.

_____

_____

_____

_____

_____

_____

_____

_____

_____

_____

_____

_____

_____

_____

_____

_____

This exercise is powerful done with compassion, granting the perspective of a future version of us, and it often reveals our hopes, wishes, and wants, helping to steer us back on track. It casts a light on what we might want to prioritise so we can recalibrate. This works extraordinarily well if it coincides with taking a digital break, while tuning out what's outside so that you can tune in to yourself.

Have those conversations

A huge part of feeling lost can lie in those around us: a parent we didn't want to disappoint, a partner who has different expectations, an overly critical colleague, people we like to feel needed by, a boss who keeps moving the goalpost, and so on.

Doing this exploratory work is vitally important but so is being honest with those who matter to us, including those with an overbearing influence, those we share the people-pleasing trap with, or, at work, the uneven distribution of power.

We'll know if a conversation is needed based on a bone of contention, which creates feelings of resentment, frustration, and anger. These are signs that our boundaries have been overstepped and need reinforcing. Whatever that much-needed, overdue conversation is, *have it*. Be clear, calm, concise and honest. Your life = your limits, and it's your responsibility to design, create, tweak, pivot, and make decisions on how you live it.

I wish I'd known that I wasn't alone

Much self-shaming comes with not being able to cope when others seem to be not only coping but doing it so, so well. We might start telling ourselves that we're weak and flawed as we try to tough-love ourselves out of it.

Any type of emotional pain can feel isolating if we're not adept at reaching out for help. There's also stigma, one-upmanship, and even discrimination to contend with. The fear that we might lose our jobs or get overlooked for progression within our workplaces is palpable.

Mixed messaging in the media adds to our confusion. On the one hand we're seeing adverts about how good it is to talk, how we must reach out and get help. Then we see the bold typeface of newspaper headlines which tear down the very people who have talked and reached out or who need to; those who appear to be under pressure, behaving differently and seeming unwell, are at best mocked, and at worst completely vilified.

Emotional pain then becomes something to hide, to keep a lid on. That makes things worse, because if we're all doing that then we aren't showing up as we are, but living in fear. We become unable to support one another because we're not aware of the support that's needed. Emotional pain layered with loneliness serves to exacerbate the pain.

When we start digging into the data of stress, it's staggering. Horrifying. Stress is so prevalent, so ingrained. It's such a huge issue with far-reaching impact that it makes one wonder why on earth more isn't being done to tackle it and prevent it. Consider:

- One in 14 UK adults (7 per cent) feel stressed every single day (Ciphr).

- 74 per cent of people feel so stressed they have been overwhelmed or unable to cope (Mental Health Foundation and YouGov).

- Inpatient hospital admissions caused by stress-related illnesses in the UK cost around £8.13bn (Statistica).

- 37 per cent of adults who reported feeling stressed also felt lonely as a result (Mental Health Foundation and YouGov).

- The UK lost 17 million working days to work-related stress, depression, or anxiety in the year 2021 to 2022 according to the latest data from the Health and Safety Executive.

• 96 per cent of small business owners admit to keeping the stress of running a business 'bottled up', with 71 per cent agreeing they often pretend to family, friends, and work colleagues that everything is okay, and 63 per cent admitting to deprioritising their mental health in the name of financial success (The British Association for Counselling and Psychotherapy).

• 79 per cent of UK workers have experienced burnout, with 35 per cent reporting high or extreme levels (Ceridian).

The truth is, we're all buckling underneath the heftiness of modern-day life. I'm sharing these findings because they reiterate our not-alone-ness and also prove, I think, that we're each doing our best within systems, practices, and processes which haven't changed with the times. In fact, some are downright archaic, and these societal frameworks don't support mental health. And in many environments, there are now simply *too* many systems, practices, and processes. We're forever trying to increase our bandwidths to encapsulate all that's thrown our way, and it's downright exhausting trying to sieve out what's important, relevant, and necessary.

It's always a work in progress

Life is unpredictable, and we're not privy to what comes next, no matter how organised or prepared we feel. The battle against stress requires constant and continuing care so that we're topped up enough to cope. I thought I'd share my present practices; they are ever-evolving, as am I.

Food as medicine

I held onto my beloved chai lattes for as long as possible until it became obvious that the subsequent sugar crash made me feel awful. Some swaps were necessary to satisfy my sweet tooth, so instead of the chai latte, it's an oat milk, cacao, and maple syrup affair. We're always stocked up on nuts and dark chocolate for snacks, and I make sure to stuff my breakfast smoothie with as many nutrients as possible, because somewhere, sometime, the way I think about food has changed from being a love language, to a fuel, an energy source, and medicine. It's still our home's love language to a degree (we made a lush cheesecake the other day) but in moderation. As someone who has numbed with food for as long as she can remember, it feels great to have got to that place.

Supplementing with adaptogens has helped balance my hormones and increase the quality of my sleep. I'm (reluctantly) sharing my current supplement stack because you'll be curious, but also want to say that the nutrients you need could well differ. It's best to start slowly and to pay attention to the effects of whatever you consume. I currently take: a blend of maca root, ashwagandha and turmeric; omega-3 fatty acids; evening primrose oil; spirulina; a daily biotic; agnus cactus; and vitamin D. I also eat two Brazil nuts every day to make sure I'm getting enough selenium.

Movement
I can't quantify the number of times I've started a walk and wanted to turn back because my head feels like it's going to explode, only to find that 30 minutes later, I've literally stomped everything out. It can be hailing, blowing a gale, or torrentially raining, and I'm still going out! These daily walks have become a crutch because of the way I feel afterwards and because I seem to sleep better for it.

Other daily stuff
I build in padding between anything that's in my diary, and I do not take work-related phone calls unless they've been scheduled in beforehand. When I was rediscovering myself and

working on what my values might be, freedom and autonomy were a big deal. They still are a big deal, as are boundaries.

If a day is getting the better of me, I'll journal through it, have an Epsom salt bath with some drops of essential oils, drink chamomile tea, listen to the Calm app on my phone, and/or wrap myself up in a blanket.

I've shaped my day in a way that works for me. I'm more creative in the mornings and earlier in the week so I focus those tasks, then. Less creative tasks and asks take place later in the day or later in the week.

Sleep is always key. I can cope with more after a string of good nights. When it's a rough night, I'm curious about why so that I can learn from it. I go to bed early and read for an hour or two (always fiction, because non-fiction gets my ideas spinning) and never have my phone in the bedroom.

Working from home means I'm often alone, so there's a balance there between being an introvert but still needing meaningful connection. I make sure I'm present when I'm with my family, and we all endeavour to do something together every day (play Uno or Monopoly, hang out or play, watch a film, or do a craft). Togetherness is the key, for me. With the right people, that is. I'm more mindful now of the energy exchange that occurs when we're with others and the impact we might have on each other. It sounds so cliché but the people we surround ourselves with makes *such* a difference.

As a previous people-pleaser, I will attest to the power

of being authentic and speaking up and out for yourself. Knowing my values has helped me tremendously to make different decisions. Also, I think having an outlet or way to express feelings, as opposed to letting them get pent-up, is crucial, whether in a journal, through therapy, or with a friend who is a great listener.

And I do not watch the news.

Working life

We spend such a large proportion of our lives working, yet often we don't enjoy the work that's eating into our days. We're just so up against it in terms of quickly running out of motivation and joy. It's taken me a long while and lots of experimenting to understand what my skills are and where they align with what I enjoy and value. Presently, my work is writing books like this one, mentoring other writers, and hosting workshops, and this feels like a sweet spot.

Can't live without

- noise cancelling headphones for the win!
- my Kindle
- Spotify – podcasts and calming playlists
- all and any blankets
- my heated seat pad for my office chair
- candles and essential oils
- plants, here, there, and everywhere

- the Calm app
- craft kits
- dark chocolate
- hugs

Over to you

These kinds of books teach us and deliver new ideas, but the power isn't in the book itself, it's in the actions we take because of what we've learned within those pages. The *smallest* changes can be and often are the most transformational and trajectory-changing.

As we've seen, stress is normalised within our society, and it's not a habitat within which anything or anyone seems to be blooming. Yet we *deserve* to bloom. Stress doesn't have to be *our* normal any longer. On the other side of all this noise, chaos, and confusion, is a place where each of us can breathe.

How do we travel from A to B? We take one step a time. What's going to be your onestep?

On this date _ _ / _ _ / _ _ _ _, I am making a self-promise to be self-helpful, and my first step is that I'm going to:

_____

_____

_____

_____

_____

_____

_____

_____

_____

_____

_____

_____

Signed:

_____

Acknowledgements

Dom, you are reverent in the way you hold space for these books to be written. With bottomless patience in your chief role of book idea sounding board, giver of endless encouraging words, asker for progress reports with sincere interest, and the supplier of all the snacks and drinks to keep me ticking along, you're a treasure, and I treasure everything about you. You feel like home and home is where the heart is. Thank you for being my lobster.

Peggy, you're a ball of energetic light and all things bright, and even that is an understatement and a half. The generous supply of hugs and placement of my books on your desk totally slay me in all the most glorious ways. You are also home and where my heart is. Thank you for being so much fun, so curious, kind, and quirky, I adore you and love you to the moon and back.

I must include our dog, Winnie, in this. I just must. He's been sitting in his dog bed by my side as this book has been written, a comforting and dependable presence. I love him.

I'm sure the only reason I'm writing at all is because of my mum. Without her loving nudge at a time when I so needed it, I don't think I'd have found my way back to my witterings and that makes me oh-so-utterly grateful. And relieved! You, Mum, are just so magnificent in every way. Our lives are so splendid, more exciting, full of love and laughter because of you. I'd choose you over, and over, and over again. Thank you for always having my back.

To Clairie, Dad, Livvy, Ro-Ro, Ammy, Wendy, Adgie, Amy, and so many others who know I love them, you are the very *best* beans. <3

The team I've worked with on this book are the shyer types so I'm not naming names but want to acknowledge the sheer level of love and care they too have poured into this book. The people you surround yourself with make a significant difference to how a project plays out and how you feel about it when you're in the thick of it. The people who have worked their socks off on this book have been such a pleasure to work with, with their love of books, enthusiasm, positivity, creativity, and expertise. I can't wait to do it all again with them soon, it's been an absolute joy. Thank you so very much.

About the author

Jayne Hardy is the author of five books, including Everything I Wish I'd Known About Stress: A Hopeful Toolkit, Kind Words for Unkind Days, and The Self-Care Project. As well as her love of writing, she mentors other writers and hosts writing workshops and sessions.

She has spoken, and written, about her own experiences of depression and self-care on BBC Radio 2 and in publications such as Huffington Post, Grazia, The Guardian, and Virgin. com, to name a few. Her TEDx talk on depression has over 400,000 views.

In 2011, Jayne founded The Blurt Foundation, a charitable organisation created to raise awareness and understanding of depression. Although she has moved on from that role, her innovative use of the internet to bring about positive social change was recognised from the off. She won the TalkTalk Digital Hero Award in 2011, and in 2014 was included in Marketing Magazine's list of Top Ten Digital Mavericks. Jayne has been mentioned as one of the 19 inspirational women leading the way in mental health by Rethink as part of their

International Women's Day celebration. In 2016, Jayne led the viral #whatyoudontsee social media campaign.

Visit https://jaynehardy.co.uk
Follow on Instagram: @JayneHardy_